EatSmart

For information address Jean Carper,
JECarper Enterprises, LLC,
PO Box 5550, Key West, Florida, 33041
or www.jeancarper.com

Library of Congress Cataloging-in-Publication Data
has been applied for.

ISBN 0-9758702-0-3

Art direction/Design: Joannah Ralston
Insight Design, insightdesign@adelphia.net

Food Photographs:
Renée Comet (*Curried Lentil Soup, Asparagus with
Balsamic Dressing, Turkey Burger, Chocolate Cake*)
Sheri Giblin (*Spring Rolls, Fish Kebabs*)
Brian Leatart (*all other food photographs*)

Cover Design: Joannah Ralson
Cover Photograph: Brian Smith

Printed and bound in USA by RR Donnelley

10 9 8 7 6 5 4 3 2 1

EatSmart

THE NUTRITION COOKBOOK
YOU CAN'T LIVE WITHOUT

BY

Jean Carper

Dedication

I would like to dedicate this book to the
millions of readers of my EatSmart column
in *USA WEEKEND* Magazine and to the
superb staff, editors and management
of *USA WEEKEND* for their vision in
persuading me to do the column and
their support, notably Marcia Bullard,
president and CEO, Jack Curry,
executive editor, and especially
Brenda Turner, managing editor.

Thank you for helping
to make this book,
commemorating ten years
of the EatSmart column,
a reality.

contents

Part 3: The Recipes

Why this book?

I have been writing a column called EatSmart for *USA WEEKEND* Magazine since 1994. One of the highpoints is being in touch with millions of Americans who read the column. At this writing, the weekly circulation of *USA WEEKEND* Magazine, published by Gannett Co. and distributed in 600 newspapers, is 19 million copies with nearly 50 million readers.

You can be sure many readers contact me by e-mail and letters with requests for reprints of the columns and recipes that they have clipped, stashed away and have now lost. Often, they suggest that I put it all together in a book. So, I did.

Obviously, I could not include all of my columns over a decade. But I have selected and updated the most popular and important columns, reporting the latest research on how to eat to keep your health, avoid or reverse chronic diseases, slow down aging, and perhaps prolong your life.

I have also chosen more than 150 of my recipes, nearly all of them previously published in *USA WEEKEND*, that seemed to be readers' favorites. Thus, the recipes have been tested by not only myself, my family and friends, but also by millons of readers.

I am by no means a chef. But I do like to make up recipes that require relatively few common ingredients, are easy and quick to make, taste good and primarily are good for you. They are typically low calorie, high in good fat, low in bad fat, low in blood-sugar-spiking activity, moderately low in sodium, and full of antioxidants from fruits and vegetables, herbs and spices. Since I do not eat red meat myself, the recipes do not contain red meat – beef, lamb, pork, veal – with one exception. For those beef-eaters, there is a recipe showing how to reduce the carcinogens formed in cooked hamburgers.

Many of the recipes are vegetarian, and many contain fish. Some also contain poultry, which appears more healthful than red meat, researchers say.

Some of the columns contain information and research on the value of specific supplements. I also take vitamins, minerals and antioxidant supplements that I formulate myself and make available to those who want them.

You can contact me at jeancarper.com where you can sign up for my free newsletter and email me with your questions and comments.

Enjoy!

Jean Carper

Jean Carper

PART 1

How to EatSmart

Ten Rules for Smart Eating

Here are the ten most important things you can do to improve your diet, boost your health, fend off disease and live longer.

1 Eat Fatty Fish

It's not just fish, but fatty fish – fresh and canned salmon, tuna, sardines, herring, mackerel – that keep arteries clear, hearts in rhythm and the brain and joints functioning well. In recent research, eating fatty fish only once a week slashed fatal heart attack risk by 44 percent.

2 Eat Whole Grains

To reduce your odds of heart disease, cancer, diabetes, obesity and premature death, eat whole grains. Examples: oatmeal, shredded wheat, whole-grain bread, popcorn, brown rice, bulgur wheat. Whole grains, unlike refined grains, deliver loads of fiber, antioxidants, anti-cancer agents, cholesterol reducers, clot-blockers, plus essential minerals, such as zinc, selenium and magnesium.

3 Use Olive Oil

People who eat lots of olive oil have better blood cholesterol and blood pressure, less heart disease, cancer (notably of the colon, breast, prostate and pancreas), less arthritis, and live the longest! New research even finds that diets rich in olive oil help prevent wrinkles. Olive oil is packed with antioxidants and good type monounsaturated fats. Best: extra virgin.

4 Eat Nuts

A daily ounce of tree nuts (walnuts, almonds, pecans) or peanuts can cut your risk of heart disease up to 50 percent. A University of Toronto study shows that a very high-fiber vegetable-grain diet, including 2.3 ounces of nuts daily, lowered bad LDL cholesterol 30 percent in a week! The diet worked as well as cholesterol-reducing "statins," such as Lipitor and Mevacor, say researchers. Eating nuts also increases longevity, according to other research.

5 Drink Tea

Real brewed tea (from bags or loose tea) has amazing powers to help detoxify the body and discourage strokes, heart attacks, cancer and neurological damage. Black and green tea are both beneficial in studies, but green teas do have about double the antioxidant activity. Green tea also possesses EGCG, a unique anti-cancer agent and possible brain cell protector against Alzheimer's and Parkinson's. To extract the most antioxidants, brew tea five minutes. Instant, bottled and herbal teas don't work; they lack antioxidants.

Eat Fruits and Vegetables

Plant foods are the best antidote to virtually all chronic ailments: high blood pressure, heart disease, diabetes, arthritis, cancer, stroke, wrinkles, obesity, age-related mental decline. Fruits and vegetables are rich cocktails of vitamins, minerals, antioxidants and fiber. Best bets: deeply colored greens, brightly colored berries and citrus fruits. Eat at least five, and preferably seven to nine servings a day.

Eat Good Carbohydrates

"Bad" carbs spike blood sugar and insulin; "good" carbs ("low glycemic index" foods) do not. Keeping insulin low is a secret to longevity, research shows. Eating good carbs such as dried beans, lentils, peanuts, oatmeal, yogurt, cherries, prunes, can help prevent colon cancer, heart disease, diabetes, obesity and poor memory.

Restrict Meat, Animal Fat and Trans Fats

All are hazardous to your health. Red meat, especially grilled or fried (as in bacon), is linked to several cancers, primarily colon cancer. Saturated fats in whole milk, butter, cheese, sausage, steaks and poultry clog arteries, encourage inflammation and are linked to cancer and degenerative brain diseases. Trans fatty acids found in many margarines, processed snack foods, and baked goods, such as donuts, are even worse for your heart than animal fats. The words "partially hydrogenated" oils mean trans fats.

Eat Less

"Cutting portion sizes in half would do more to improve Americans' health than anything," says one expert. Compelling research shows that obesity is a major cause of disease and premature death. Eating excessive calories accelerates aging, leads to obesity and contributes to cancer, heart disease, diabetes and Alzheimer's disease. Drastically trimming calories is the only reliable way known to increase life span in animals.

Take a Multivitamin/Mineral Pill

The supplement is insurance against nutritional inadequacies that can promote chronic diseases. A lack of micronutrients – such as folic acid, vitamin B12 and B6, niacin, vitamin C and E, and zinc – actually damages genetic DNA the same way radiation and chemical carcinogens do, setting the stage for cancer, according to landmark studies by researchers at the University of California at Berkeley. Correcting even minor deficiencies can boost immunity, curb chronic diseases and perhaps prolong life.

Fats

The good, the bad and the ugly

A guide to dietary fats

Contrary to popular belief, not all fat is bad. Your body needs good fats to survive and thrive. Indeed, the *type* of fat you eat is far more important than the *amount* of fat you eat. For example, the lifesaving Mediterranean diet is high in fat (as much as 40 percent of calories), but most of it is good fat from olive oil and fish. In one large study, eaters of a Mediterranean diet had 70 percent lower death rates from all causes than eaters of a low-fat American-type heart diet (about 30 percent calories from fat.)

Indeed, long-term Harvard studies have never found any link between a high percentage of calories from fat and any important disease, including heart disease, cancer and weight gain. But they have found that the type of fat you eat can dramatically affect your health.

. . . .

Bad Fats

- **Animal fats including butter, cheese, lard and the fat contained in meat, poultry and milk:** Most experts agree that the saturated fat in animal products is a prime enemy in raising bad cholesterol, promoting inflammation and clogging arteries, leading to cardiovascular disease. It may harm immune functioning and increase risk of cancer, diabetes and cognitive decline, including Alzheimer's, as you grow older.
- **Corn oil:** A risky choice, high in omega-6 fatty acids. In a six-month study by Harvard researcher George L. Blackburn, daily doses of corn oil doubled the odds of recurrence and spread of colon cancer.

Corn oil is also rapidly oxidized (saturated with oxygen), releasing floods of disease-causing free radicals inside the body. Experts say nearly everyone should cut back on corn oil, regular safflower and sunflower seed oils (all laden with omega-6 fatty acids).

So-So Fats

- **Soybean oil:** Okay sometimes. Best when eaten in tofu (soybean curd) and whole soybeans, which also contain antioxidants. Soybean oil contains desirable monounsaturated fatty acids , but is also high in hazardous omega-6 fatty acids that can overrun cells, promoting cancer,

GOOD FATS

- **Olive oil:** Its fat is mainly monounsaturated, which promotes health. Studies show that people whose main source of fat is olive oil live longer and have less heart disease, cancer and arthritis. Olive oil also contains antioxidants, similar to those in tea and red wine, which combat disease processes. Best choice: Extra virgin olive oil.

- **Fish oil (omega-3 fat):** Overwhelming research shows omega-3 oils in fatty fish can help save you from cardiovascular disease, (especially sudden cardiac death), cancer, respiratory problems, inflammatory conditions (such as arthritis) and neurological disorders (including depression) and Alzheimer's disease. Best sources of omega 3s: salmon, herring, sardines, tuna, both canned and fresh. Eat fish at least twice a week. Even one weekly serving conveys great benefits. *Caution:* The government warns pregnant women and small children to restrict intake of certain fish because of potential toxic contamination (See page 12).

- **Canola oil:** Excellent, because it's very low in saturated fat, high in monounsaturated fat and rich in beneficial omega-3 fatty acids. Use it in salad dressings, for sautéing or frying, or in any recipe that calls for cooking oil.

- **Macadamia nut oil:** Excellent. Highest of all salad oils in monounsaturated fats.

- **High Oleic-Acid Safflower Oil:** Excellent. It ranks high as a monounsaturated fat, along with olive oil. Previously, safflower oil consisted mainly of less desirable omega-6 type fatty acids. Now most safflower oil is about 75 percent good oleic-acid of the type in olive oil. Be sure the label on safflower oil indicates "high oleic-acid."

- **Grapeseed oil:** Good. In studies, it has raised good HDL cholesterol. High in antioxidants.

- **Avocado oil:** Okay. Like avocados, it's rich in beneficial monounsaturated fat.

- **Walnut oil:** OK. High in beneficial plant omega-3's.

inflammatory reactions and immune function. Although safer than corn oil, soybean oil is not nearly as healthful as olive oil and canola oil. Unfortunately, much soybean oil is hydrogenated – or hardened – making it particularly harmful.

- **Peanut oil:** Okay to use sometimes. It is very similar in fatty acid composition to soybean oil. Use only occasionally.
- **Tropical fats such as palm and coconut oils:** Other vegetable fats have little saturated fat, but these tropical fats are

50 to 85 percent saturated fat. Nevertheless, they appear not to destroy arteries. Research shows they raise good HDL blood cholesterol. They also are high in lauric acid, found to be anti-inflammatory, antiviral and antibacterial. Okay to eat occasionally.

What About Flaxseed Oil?

Flaxseed oil, usually taken as a supplement, is rich in omega-3 fatty acids and appears to have anti-cancer benefits. However, it is far less potent than omega 3s in fish oil. Generally, it takes 10 grams of flaxseed oil to equal one gram of fish oil, says Artemis Simopoulos, M.D., president of the Center for Genetics, Nutrition and Health and author of *The Omega Diet* (HarperCollins 1999). The reason: flaxseed oil is a short-chain plant omega-3 that needs to be converted by the body to beneficial long-chain omega-3 fatty acids (DHA and EPA) found in seafood.

If you depend entirely on flaxseed oil for omega 3, you need roughly a daily tablespoon of flaxseed oil (7,000 mg plant omega 3) to get a recommended daily 650 milligrams of EPA and DHA concentrated in fatty fish, such as salmon and sardines. Getting long-chain omega-3 fatty acids from fish is much more efficient and dependable.

What About Cholesterol?

Cholesterol-rich foods, such as eggs and shrimp, pose little or no threat to most people. A recent comprehensive analysis of 224 scientific studies over 25 years by Wanda Howell, Ph.D., University of Arizona, concludes that eating cholesterol only slightly affects blood cholesterol. The primary villain is saturated animal fat, she says. A recent British study showed that cutting out 50 milligrams of dietary cholesterol a day reduces blood cholesterol less than one point.

In a large Harvard study, men and women who ate an egg a day did not have more heart attacks than those who ate an egg only once a week. So an egg a day (rich in choline, needed for brain development and B vitamins that may discourage heart disease) is generally ok, say most experts.

Trans Fats: The Worst Fat of All

Of all fats, the ugliest – more vicious even than animal fat – are trans fats. Such fats are created when liquid oils are solidified by a process called partial hydrogenation that stretches processed foods' shelf life and changes "safe" unsaturated fats into dangerous ones. Trans fats are concentrated in solid vegetable shortenings, hard stick margarines, donuts, crackers, cookies, chips, some cereals, cakes, pies, some breads, and foods that have been fried in hydrogenated fats, such as chicken, fish and potatoes.

Harvard nutritionist Walter Willett blames trans fats for at least 30,000 premature deaths a year, calling their introduction into the diet the "biggest food-processing disaster in U.S. history."

Mary G. Enig, Ph.D., a pioneering trans-fats researcher, formerly at the University of Maryland, says: "Several decades of research show that consumption of trans fats promotes heart disease, cancer, diabetes, immune dysfunction, obesity, and reproductive problems."

What's bad about trans fats?

About everything, when it comes to blood fats that affect the heart, says Willett. Mainly, trans fats increase bad LDL cholesterol, triglycerides, and insulin levels, reduce beneficial HDL cholesterol and promote inflammation that helps bring on heart attacks. Harvard research found a one-and-a-half times higher heart attack risk in women who ate the most trans-fats, primarily in margarine, compared with women eating the least. In men, the risk was more than double.

Margarine, a special villain. Margarine accounts for about 20 to 25 percent of all trans fats consumed, says Dr. Enig. Eating an extra teaspoon of trans-fat rich margarine a day boosted men's chances of heart attack 10 percent, according to the famed Framingham Heart Study. Generally, the harder the margarine, the more the trans

> When trans fatty acids are absorbed into human cell membranes, they create abnormal body chemistry which can cause fat deposits in the arteries, liver and other organs, potentially leading to heart attack, stroke or circulatory occlusion.
>
> −National Nutritional Foods Association

fat. Recent Tufts research shows that eating hard stick margarine sent triglycerides 18 percent higher than did semi-liquid squeeze-bottle margarine.

In fact, trans-fat rich margarines are worse for cholesterol than butter. Butter's saturated fat raises bad LDL, but margarine's trans fats both boost LDL and depress good HDL cholesterol, doubling the damage. Recent Dutch research found that trans fats depressed good HDL cholesterol 21 percent more than saturated fats did. Thus, eating trans fats is extra harmful if you already have low HDLs, warn experts. Further, trans fats raise Lp(a), another artery-destroying blood fat.

Trans fats promote other health hazards:

Cancer. Dutch researchers found elevated trans fats in the breast tissue of women with breast cancer. A recent University of North Carolina study reported that a high consumption of sweetened baked goods and oils and condiments high in trans fats doubled the odds of colon polyps that may lead to cancer.

Reproductive Problems: Pregnant and lactating women should minimize intake of trans fats. Recent research shows that pregnant women with the highest levels of a common trans fat had seven times the risk of the complication preeclampsia, characterized by high blood pressure and edema. High trans fats may also harm fetal

HOW TO AVOID TRANS FATS

- Use olive oil and canola oil for virtually all cooking.

- Use trans-fat-free margarines – soft tub or liquid margarines instead of hard, stick margarines. Generally, the softer the margarine the better, and liquid is the best. A tablespoon of stick margarine has about 1.9 grams of trans fat, a tablespoon of regular tub margarine, .8 grams. Check the label for trans-free brands. By government standards, trans-fat-free means less than .5 grams per serving.

- Try to avoid foods made with "partially hydrogenated" oils, as listed on labels. The higher "partially hydrogenated" appears in the ingredient list, the more trans fats. Special hazards: baked goods. Half a cookie's fat may be trans fats. A donut contains from 4 to 9 grams of trans fats.

- If a label doesn't list trans fats, you can get a rough figure by adding grams of saturated fat, monounsaturated fat, and polyunsaturated fat, and subtracting that figure from total fat grams. The difference is the grams of trans fat per serving.

- When eating out, avoid deep fried foods, apt to be oozing trans fats. A batter-dipped deep-fried whole onion – an appetizer popular at steak houses – has 18 grams of trans fats, according to the Center for Science in the Public Interest. Other trans-fat horrors: cheese fries, onion rings, fried clams, fish, scallops and shrimp, fried chicken.

and infant development. Nursing mothers who eat trans fats pass them on to infants during breast feeding. Infants feasting on trans fats may have diminished visual acuity and brain development.

Diabetes: Trans fats appear to reduce the body's ability to handle blood sugar by lowering responses to the hormone insulin, which is particularly dangerous to diabetics.

How much trans fat is okay for the heart? Virtually none, according to a recent analysis of 59 heart-diet studies by Dutch researcher Peter L. Zock at the Wageningen Centre for Food Sciences. He finds the best diet strategy is not to lower total fat, but to severely restrict saturated fats and to get trans-fats intake to near zero.

Why Fish Can Save Your Life

Eat fish! You've heard it before, but now the case for fish oil is so compelling that you absolutely must pay attention or face overwhelming health risks.

Fish's secret is its unique oil, called omega-3 fatty acids, essential for proper cell functioning. But most Americans get only 15 percent of what they need.

Here's How Eating Fish Protects You

- **Stops Fatal Heart Attacks:** More than 250,000 Americans die suddenly of heart attacks every year; half have no warning signs. Yet, eating fatty fish could stop an astonishing 80 percent of such unexpected deaths in men, says new Harvard research, involving 22,000 male physicians. It's the first time fish oil has been found lifesaving in people with no history of heart disease. The higher the men's blood omega-3 fats, the lower their risk of death. A probable reason: fish oil helps suppress arrythmias (irregular heartbeats) that can trigger cardiac arrest.

- **Prevents Heart Disease:** The more often women eat fish, the less likely they are to have a heart attack or die of a "cardiac event," says other Harvard research, tracking 85,000 female nurses. Eating fish only once a week cut heart attack risk 29 percent; the figure jumped to 34 percent in women who ate fish five times a week. Researchers credit the omega-3 fat in fish.

- **Cuts Strokes:** Fish was even more dramatic in preventing strokes in the nurses. Women who ate fish more than five times a week suffered only half as many strokes as occasional fish eaters, primarily strokes due to blood clots.

- **Blocks Cancer:** Recent research in France found that women with the highest amounts of omega-3s in breast fatty tissue were nearly 70 percent less apt to have breast cancer than women with the least omega-3s. In a new Swedish study, women who ate fatty fish (salmon and herring) twice a week cut their risk of endometrial cancer by 40 percent, compared with women who ate fatty fish less than once a month. Eating lean fish, such as cod and flounder, did not reduce cancer risk. The same Swedish investigators found that prostate cancer rates were two or three times higher in non-fish eaters than in men who ate moderate or high amounts of fish.

- **Soothes Brains, Saves Memory:** Fish eaters around the world are less apt to be depressed, violent and suicidal. One probable reason: omega-3s boost serotonin, the brain's feel-good chemical. Low blood omega-3s also predict a greater risk of memory loss and Alzheimer's disease as you age. In fact, in a study of 815 older men and women in China, those who ate fish once a week or more reduced their risk of developing Alzheimer's disease by an amazing 60 percent, compared with those who rarely or never ate fish. In Israeli research, short-term memory improved in 74 percent and long-term memory in 58 percent of Alzheimer's patients given fish oil. Fish oil is essential for fetal and infant brains. In Danish research, pregnant women who ate fish once a week cut their risk of premature delivery by a third.

Seafood Safety

- **Caution:** The Food and Drug Administration advises pregnant women, women who plan to become pregnant, nursing mothers and young children to restrict fish with higher levels of methyl mercury, a potential neurological toxin.

This means such women and children should:
- Avoid eating shark, swordfish, king mackerel and tilefish.
- Eat no more than six ounces a week of albacore tuna, often sold as canned white tuna; it tends to have more mercury than other tuna.
- Limit canned "light" tuna, lower in mercury, to 12 ounces a week.

- **Safest:** Seafood with very low or undetectable levels of mercury include: salmon, flounder/sole, tilapia, catfish and shellfish (crab, scallops, oysters, shrimp, clams) say government figures. However, you can't count on lean white fish or shellfish for much omega-3 fat.

Generally, your best choice for high omega-3 with a low risk of contaminants is salmon. Also sardines; small fish are less apt to be contaminated. But you should not depend on just one source. Eat a variety of fatty fish to get omega-3s. Don't eat fish skin; it's a prime site of toxic contaminants.

- **Farm-raised versus wild salmon:** Contrary to popular belief, farmed salmon contains as much omega-3 healthy oils as wild salmon, says the U.S. Department of Agriculture. But there are other concerns. Farmed salmon is fed artificial color, may pollute the ocean and may contain more environmental toxins called PCBs. Unfortunately fresh wild salmon is costly and not always available. Tip: buy canned. Almost all canned salmon is wild. Still, most experts agree that the health benefits of all salmon – wild, farmed or canned – far outweigh potential hazards.

The Fish with the Most Omega 3s

The fattiest fish have the highest concentrations of omega 3s.

Tops are mackerel, anchovies, herring, sardines, salmon, tuna, halibut, turbot, bluefish, trout, sablefish.

Fish with moderate to low omega-3s include catfish, cod, dolphin fish, flounder, grouper, haddock, perch, pike, red snapper. Shellfish generally have low levels of omega-3 fats.

HOW MUCH OMEGA 3 DO YOU NEED?

People who typically eat 2,000 calories a day need at least 650 milligrams daily of omega 3s, say experts. You can get that much by eating one of the following every day.

1.0 ounce	fresh mackerel*	3.4 ounces	canned albacore white tuna
1.4 ounces	canned sardines	3.5 ounces	swordfish*
1.6 ounces	pickled herring	7.0 ounces	grouper*
1.7 ounces	fresh salmon*	12.0 ounces	haddock*
1.9 ounces	canned salmon		
2.0 ounces	fresh tuna*	*weight before cooking	

How to Get the Most from Fish

- **Best cooking methods:** baking, poaching, steaming, microwaving, stir-frying, sautéing in a little canola or olive oil, or simmering as in fish stew. Deep-frying can destroy fish benefits.
- **Cut Back on Bad Fats:** So-called pro-inflammatory omega-6 fats, found in corn oil, regular safflower and sunflower seed oils, margarines, shortenings and to a lesser extent in soybean oil, can overwhelm and neutralize the omega 3s in your cells. So if you eat a salad dressing made with corn oil or soybean oil along with salmon, the omega-3 benefits are diminished.

Critically important is the ratio of good omega-3 to bad omega-6 fats. You should not eat more than four times as much omega-6 fat as omega-3 fat. Unfortunately, Americans eat 10 to 20 times more "bad" omega 6s than good omega 3s.

On a regular basis this can be disastrous. Many experts blame our excess of omega-6s and deficiency of omega-3s for much of our epidemic of chronic diseases, including cardiovascular disease, inflammatory diseases, such as arthritis and asthma, and mood and memory disturbances, including Alzheimer's.

Good Carbs Bad Carbs
How to Tell the Difference

The biggest myth about carbohydrates is that they are all equal in the way they affect the body. But that's far from true. It is a monumental mistake to lump all carbs together. When you eat a carbohydrate – any sugary or starchy food – your blood sugar goes up. If your blood sugar rises slowly, good. If it soars quickly, it can be a serious health threat. What really matters is how much and how fast a carbohydrate spikes your blood sugar.

"It's become quite clear that not all carbohydrates are the same," says Harvard nutritionist Walter Willett. "It's not only the amount of carbohydrate you eat, it's the type that matters." Pioneering researchers Jennie Brand-Miller, Ph.D. at University of Sydney in Australia, and Thomas M.S. Wolever M.D., Ph.D at the University of Toronto, Canada agree, as they explain in their excellent book *The*

New Glucose Revolution (Marlowe & Company, 2002).

Here's the gist. There's a vast difference between the way your body processes carbohydrates from white bread and from peanuts, for example. Eating white bread quickly sends blood sugar levels sky high. Peanuts induce blood sugar to rise gradually and only moderately. Chronic blood sugar spikes are linked to weight gain,

The Glycemic Load of 25 Common Foods

The lower the figure, the less apt the food is to spike blood sugar.

Peanuts................1	Oatmeal, regular, cooked.........9	Bagel, white.............................25
Carrots, peeled boiled.................2	Wonderbread.........................11	Potato, baked.........................26
Kellogg's All-Bran.................4	Apple juice.........................12	Mars bar.............................27
Lentils.................5	Banana.............................13	Raisins.............................28
Grainy breads.................6	Coca Cola.........................14	
Apple.................6	Donut, cake.........................17	
M&M's, peanut.................6	Spaghetti, white, boiled 5 minutes.........18	For the glycemic ratings of hundreds of other foods, search online at www.glycemicindex.com or consult *The New Glucose Revolution* and other books by authority Jennie Brand-Miller.
Baked beans.................7		
Chick peas.................8	Sushi, average.........................19	
Microwave popcorn.................8	Jelly beans.........................22	
Ice cream, average.................8	Corn Flakes.........................24	

heart disease, diabetes, some cancers, premature aging and poor intellectual functioning and memory loss in older people.

Thus, diets high in the wrong carbohydrates may do you in. But the right carbs can dramatically improve your health. The key is knowing the difference.

To determine a carb's blood-sugar raising capacity, Dr. Brand-Miller and colleagues have fed specific foods to carefully chosen groups of individuals and measured how high and how rapidly blood sugar rises. A food gets a high "glycemic index" (GI) number if it causes blood sugar to spike, and a low glycemic index number if it induces gradual rises in blood sugar. A food with a GI of under 55 is considered low-glycemic. For example, lentils have a low GI of 29. But since how much you eat of a carb also matters, researchers now calculate the blood sugar-raising power in a common serving of various foods; this is called its glycemic load or GL.

How "Bad" Carbs Can Harm You

High glycemic foods that trigger a jump in blood sugar increase your odds of chronic diseases.

- **Heart Disease:** Blood-sugar-boosting carbs double women's risk of heart disease, according to a major Harvard study. The higher the load of high glycemic foods, the greater the odds of fatal and nonfatal heart attacks.
- **Diabetes:** Bad carbs double or triple your risk of developing type 2 diabetes, according to about 15 studies.
- **Weight:** High glycemic carbs frustrate your attempts to lose weight. A low-glycemic index diet is an excellent way to control overeating and weight gain. In studies of obese teenage boys, those eating high glycemic foods consumed 80 percent more calories over a certain period than those on a low-glycemic index diet, reported researchers at Children's Hospital in Boston.

- **Cholesterol:** The wrong carbs depress good HDL cholesterol, find British researchers. The best dietary way to raise HDLs, they found, was a low-glycemic diet. Also, substituting low-glycemic index foods for high-glycemic index foods in a low fat diet, lowers blood triglycerides by 15 to 25 percent, says research at the State University of New York at Buffalo.
- **Insulin resistance:** Blood sugar jumps lead to "insulin resistance" that promotes high blood pressure, clogged arteries, heart attacks and strokes. Eating

---

BOTTOM LINE:
Eating a low-glycemic diet is one of the best ways to improve overall health, control weight, ward off disease and prolong life.

---

a low-glycemic index diet for a month has reversed insulin resistance.

- **Inflammation:** High glycemic carbs incite inflammation in blood vessels, which new research identifies as a culprit in heart disease, strokes and Alzheimer's disease. Harvard research found nine times more inflammation in the blood of women who ate the highest glycemic-index foods, compared with those who ate the lowest glycemic foods.

- **Cancer:** Bad carbs encourage certain cancers. Italian women eating the highest as opposed to the lowest glycemic index diet were 40 percent more apt to develop breast cancer. Harvard research suggests that women who are overweight and inactive more than double their risk of pancreatic cancer by eating a very high GL diet compared with a very low one. Both colon and breast cancers have also been tied to consuming high GL diets.

- **Aging:** The wrong carbs can damage cells, causing accelerated aging of all tissues and organs, according to University of California, Berkeley, researchers. Plain sugar (sucrose) especially, produces signs of accelerated aging in cells.

A QUICK GUIDE TO THE BEST CARBS

- Choose whole grain foods over highly processed ones.
- Eat more legumes (dried beans, lentils and peanuts).
- Restrict "white" foods, such as sugar, white bread and white potatoes.
- Eat more high-fiber fruits and vegetables.
- Restrict sugary soft drinks and other high sugar beverages.
- Eat spaghetti undercooked (al dente); avoid canned spaghetti.
- Add vinegar or lemon juice to carbs; the acid lowers the glycemic index.
- Choose sourdough bread over other breads.
- Choose oatmeal and All-Bran over highly processed cereals.
- Choose basmati or Uncle Ben's converted rice; they are lower glycemic index than brown or white rice. Instant rice is high.

SIX WAYS TO CONTROL BAD CARBS

Eat lots of legumes. They are digested slowly, causing gradual rises in blood sugar, and thus have low ratings. These include baked beans, butter beans, lentils, chick peas, kidney beans, navy beans, soybeans and peanuts (which technically are legumes, not nuts).

Know your starches. White potatoes and white rice can raise blood sugar faster and higher than eating candy. Sushi rice (made with vinegar), basmati rice, brown rice and especially Uncle Ben's converted rice have a lower glycemic index. Dr. Brand-Miller also says it's a myth that pasta makes you fat. All pastas, says Dr. Brand-Miller are fairly low-glycemic, helping dampen blood sugar, appetite and weight gain. You can lower pasta's glycemic index by undercooking it – to the "al dente" stage.

Add vinegar or lemon juice to foods. Studies show eating 4 teaspoons of vinegar in a salad dressing with an average meal lowers blood sugar as much as 30 percent. Brand-Miller found that adding vinegar to high-index white potatoes reduced expected blood sugar surges by 25 percent. The reason: acid slows stomach emptying and digestion. She advises eating a salad with a vinegar or lemon-juice dressing with high-glycemic meals. Drinking orange and grapefruit juice also may help. Acidity explains why yogurt and sourdough bread have low GI ratings.

Combine high and low glycemic index foods. If you eat high-glycemic foods, combining them, such as dried beans and rice, for example, produces an intermediate glycemic index rating. When you eat snacks alone, choose snacks with a low rating, such as apples, peanuts or popcorn. A high-glycemic food, such as jelly beans, eaten alone is sure to spike your blood sugar.

Eat lots of vegetables. You can think of salad vegetables as "free" foods, with no significant impact on blood sugar. Their glycemic rating is effectively "zero," says Brand-Miller. Meat does not raise blood sugar, but its fat promotes insulin resistance. It's important to restrict high-fat foods as well as high-glycemic-index foods, she cautions.

Restrict processed foods. Bread, cereals, cookies and crackers made with finely ground flour have a high rating because the fine particles of starch zip right through your digestive tract. Many cereals and breads have a rating of 70 or more, higher than table sugar's 60-65. Some cold cereals with a low rating: All-Bran with extra fiber, Bran Buds with psyllium, Special K, muesli.

Eat Fiber
Live Longer

B Basically, fiber is the stuff in food that doesn't get fully digested. Two types exist: water-soluble (found in oats, legumes, fruits, whole grains and some vegetables) and insoluble (wheat bran).

How Eating High Fiber Helps You:

Stay alive. A recent British report shows that men and women who ate the most fiber cut their odds of death from all causes by one third during the 11-year study, compared to the skimpiest fiber eaters. Surprisingly, fiber was more powerful than antioxidant intake in staving off death. High fiber cut the risk of heart disease in women by nearly half.

Stay slim. In a study of 2,900 young adults by Boston's Children's Hospital, those who ate the most fiber gained five percent less weight than those who ate the least. In fact, fiber was more important in preventing weight gain than fat was in promoting it. Probable reason: Fiber suppresses insulin, tied to hunger. Conclusion: High-fiber diets may protect against obesity and heart disease by cutting insulin levels.

Improve your heart. The Boston study, like many others, found that high-fiber foods lower bad LDL cholesterol, blood pressure and triglycerides, risk factors for heart disease. A major Harvard study has found that women who ate 23 grams of fiber a day, mostly from cereal, were 23 percent less likely to suffer a heart attack than those who ate 11 grams a day. In men, a high-fiber diet slashed the odds of heart attack by 36 percent.

Fight cancer. Two new studies show that a high fiber diet dramatically slashes colon cancer risk. In the largest diet-cancer study ever done, researchers studied the diets of 519,978 subjects in ten European countries for four-and-a-half years. Those who ate the most dietary fiber (35 grams a day) had a 40 percent lower risk of colon cancer than those who ate the least fiber – 15 grams a day or less. Another American study found that eating more than 30 grams of fiber daily reduced the risk of polyps that can lead to colon cancer by 20 percent compared with those who ate less than 15 grams per day. High fiber may also help prevent cancers of the breast, stomach, thyroid and mouth.

Protect your gut. A diet high in fiber, especially wheat bran, helps prevent diverticulosis, pockets in the intestinal wall that afflict half of Americans over age 60. Diverticulosis is due to years and years of lack of fiber, say gastroenterologists. Plus: A high-fiber diet can halve the risk of ulcers and cut the risk of gallstones by a third.

Easy Ways to Eat More Fiber

If your current diet is low in fiber, add high-fiber foods gradually and drink plenty of water.

- Eat high-fiber cereals. Check labels; some cereals have zero fiber; others have as much as 13 grams per serving. An acceptable cereal should have at least 3 grams of fiber per serving, preferably more.
- Top cereals with fresh berries, apples, pears or dried fruit.
- Eat whole-wheat or whole-grain bread with at least two grams of fiber per slice.
- Use less-processed grains, such as brown rice and whole-grain pasta.
- Add dried beans to stews, casseroles, soups.

HOW MUCH FIBER DO YOU NEED?

Adults: Experts advise 20 to 35 grams a day. Most Americans eat half that.

Children: Add five to their age to get the recommended amount of fiber. That means 13 grams daily for an eight-year-old. Only one-third of American children between ages seven and ten eat the recommended amount of fiber.

SUPER SOURCES OF FIBER

FOOD	FIBER GRAMS	FOOD	FIBER GRAMS
1/3 cup All-Bran Bran Buds	13.0	1/2 cup oat bran	6.0
1/2 cup All-Bran Extra Fiber	13.0	1/2 cup corn or green peas	4.5
1/2 cup Fiber One	13.0	1/4 cup almonds	4.0
1/2 cup lentils	9.0	1 large pear or apple, with skin	4.0
1/2 cup kidney beans	8.0	1 orange	3.6
1/2 cup barley	7.0	4 prunes	3.0

Grains
The Whole Truth

Eat two to three whole grain foods a day.

That simple act may do more to keep you healthy than any other dietary change, says new convincing evidence. But, if you're like 80 percent of Americans, you eat less than one serving of whole grains per day, and you're probably not even sure what a whole grain food actually is.

What Whole Grain Means

Whole grain foods are made with intact kernels, rather than with "refined" or crushed, processed kernels. Whole grains are characterized by high fiber (whole wheat has five times the fiber of refined wheat, for example.) But whole grains have much more. Whole grains are rich in an array of disease-fighting chemicals – antioxidants, tumor suppressors, cholesterol reducers, insulin regulators, antithrombotic agents, phytoestrogens and nutrients vitamin E, folic acid, zinc, selenium and magnesium.

Whole grains are what our ancestors ate for 10,000 years before modern food processing began pulverizing kernels into superfine powder, reducing their health value and robbing our bodies of protection against chronic diseases.

When whole wheat flour is refined, it is stripped of 95 percent of its vitamin E, 87 percent of its vitamin B6, 85 percent of its magnesium, 52 percent of its selenium, 40 percent of its folic acid and vitamin B12. Recent research shows how essential it is

to return to a diet of whole grains. In fact, new findings even suggest that you will live longer if you eat whole grains.

How Whole Grains Protect You

Slash Heart Disease: In a large 1999 Harvard study, women who ate 2.5 servings of whole grains a day were one-third to one-half less apt to get or die of heart disease than women eating less than half a serving daily. Strongest heart-savers: whole-grain breakfast cereals, brown rice, popcorn and bran. In fact, eating a daily bowl of cold breakfast cereal (with about 5 grams of fiber) cuts your chances of heart disease by about one-third, researchers said.

Block Cancer. Eating lots of whole grains lowers your cancer risk – as much as 50 percent for stomach and colon cancer, 40 percent for ovarian, 20 percent for prostate and pancreatic cancer, and ten percent for breast cancer, recent Italian research finds.

Ward off Diabetes. Three daily servings of whole grains cut the risk of type 2 diabetes by 21 percent in a recent University of Minnesota study of 36,000 women. In the

Harvard study, women who ate the equivalent of a bowl of oatmeal and two pieces of whole-wheat bread were only one-third as apt to develop type 2 diabetes as women who ate the least whole grain foods. Researchers credit multiple factors in whole grains that keep blood sugar and insulin under control.

Promote GI Health: Unquestionably, whole-grain, high-fiber foods are the best medicine for keeping stools soft and bulky. This not only combats constipation, but helps prevent diverticular disease, a potentially serious irritation and inflammation of tiny pouches inside the colon.

Suppress Appetite: When you eat whole grains, you're less hungry, less likely to overeat and less likely to gain weight, because whole grains are high in fiber and tend to have a low glycemic index – that is, less ability to spike blood sugar, says Tufts University's Susan Roberts, Ph.D.

Look for Whole Grain Cereals

Many cereal boxes now state whether the cereal is whole grain. More than 30 name-brand cereals are whole grain foods, says a recent industry report. You can't go wrong with these six cereals that boast more than 90 percent whole grain: Cheerios, regular (not instant) oatmeal, shredded wheat, Wheaties, Nutrigrain Golden Wheat, Toasty-O's. For others, check labels for "whole grain" or "rich in whole grain."

Whole Grains:

Wild rice, brown rice (including instant), popcorn, bulgur wheat, whole wheat kernels, wheat berries, oats and oatmeal, barley (including pearled barley), buckwheat, kasha (buckwheat groats), cracked wheat, quinoa (pronounced keenwa), amaranth.

Not Whole Grains:

White rice, cornmeal and whole-kernel corn (it's a vegetable).

An exception: All-Bran cereal is not technically whole grain, but University of Minnesota researcher Joanne Slavin, Ph.D., says it's so "loaded with bran" it has the value of whole grain. So it's kind of an "honorary" whole grain.

Check the Labels

The only way to be sure bread, pasta, crackers, etc. are whole grain is to read the labels very carefully. It can be tricky. Some breads, for example, say "seven grain," or "bran," or "made with wheat flour," giving the impression it's whole grain when it isn't. In order to be a whole grain food, the first ingredient on the label list must have the word "whole" in it, such as whole wheat (another name is graham flour), whole oats, whole rye flour, whole barley. Look for whole-wheat crackers such as Triscuits, whole-wheat tortillas and whole-grain bagels, couscous and pasta.

Don't Look for Short Cuts

Important: There's no way to find a substitute for whole grains – no short cuts, no supplements. Researchers aren't even sure which of whole grains' many components account for their remarkable disease-fighting powers. It's probably not any individual chemical, such as fiber or folic acid. That's why you have to eat the grain's "entire package," to get its benefits, say experts.

Strong Medicines
In
Fruits and
Vegetables

C an you name the four new food groups? No, they're not bread, dairy, meat and blah stuff like that. The new groups are red, orange-yellow, green and blue-purple, according to Tufts University professor James Joseph, Ph.D., the neuroscientist who discovered that eating blueberries, spinach and strawberries makes aging mice smarter.

Dr. Joseph says fruits and vegetables fight disease, and especially those that are deeply and brightly colored – red, orange-yellow, green and blue-purple. The more brilliant and intense a food's pigment, the greater the food's disease-fighting properties.

Extensive research shows that eating fruits and vegetables helps protect against cancer, heart disease, stroke, high blood pressure, asthma, diabetes, cataracts, inflammatory diseases and pulmonary troubles. The main reason: Pigments in fruits and vegetables contain phytochemicals or antioxidants that act as cancer inhibitors, cholesterol regulators, anti-inflammatories and brain cell protectors.

Each fruit and vegetable is a unique package, so you need to eat a variety to get the broadest spectrum of protection. For example, eat purple grapes and blueberries to get "anthocyanins," and tomatoes and corn to get red and yellow "carotenoids." Different antioxidants protect different organs.

ANTIOXIDANT FACTS AND ADVICE

- Frozen fruits and vegetables are as potent as fresh.
- Cooking tomatoes and carrots activates antioxidants.
- When possible, eat the colorful skins, which hold the most antioxidants.
- Always choose the brightest, deepest colors. For example, pick broccoli that is deep blue-green, not yellowish.
- Ripe fruits and vegetables contain the most antioxidants.
- Juices count. Citrus juice in particular is linked to lower disease risk.
- Dried fruits, notably prunes (dried plums) and raisins, have extremely high concentrations of antioxidants.
- Be sure to eat deep-green vegetables such as collard or mustard greens; they're the most neglected of all, and are packed with antioxidants.

EIGHT GREAT REASONS TO EAT FRUITS AND VEGETABLES

1 Heart disease risk plunged 72 percent in men and women who ate more than five fruits and vegetables a day, compared with those who ate less than one a day, finds a large Greek study.

2 Women who ate the most dark yellow-orange and green vegetables had 20 to 35 percent lower odds of breast cancer in Vanderbilt University research.

3 Eating fruit and vegetables every day reduced deaths from liver, stomach and lung cancer by 20 to 35 percent, according to new Japanese research.

4 Eating lots of fruit as a child cuts risk of cancer as an adult by almost 40 percent, finds a British study.

5 Men and women who ate the most fruits and vegetables were 20 percent less likely to have heart disease, according to Harvard research. Adding just one fruit or vegetable a day cuts heart disease risk by 4 percent.

6 In a recent Dutch study of male smokers, those who ate the most fruit were only half as likely to die of lung cancer as those who ate the least.

7 Eating more fruits and vegetables is more effective at combating excess weight than eating less high-fat/high-sugar food, according to recent research at the State University of New York, Buffalo.

8 Women who eat at least five daily servings of fruits and vegetables reduce their risk of diabetes by 40 percent compared with women who don't eat them daily, according to a study by the federal Centers for Disease Control and Prevention.

GET YOUR QUOTA

Servings of fruits and vegetables recommended by the National Cancer Institute:

Children: at least five daily servings
Women: at least seven daily servings
Men: at least nine daily servings.

What is a serving?

- One medium piece of fruit, such as apple, pear, banana
- 1 cup leafy greens, such as spinach and lettuce
- ½ cup chopped vegetables, raw or cooked
- ½ cup chopped fruit, raw or cooked
- 6 ounces fruit juice or vegetable juice

GET YOUR ANTIOXIDANTS HERE!

Here's how common fruits and vegetables stack up in total antioxidant capacity (TAC), according to the U.S. Department of Agriculture. The higher the TAC, the greater their antioxidant activity.

Fruit	Total Antioxidant Capacity (TAC)
Apples	
Fuji	1....3578
Gala	1....3903
Golden Delicious	1...3685
Granny Smith	1....5381
Red Delicious	1...5900
Apricots	1...469
Avocado, Haas	1...3344
Banana	1....1037
Blackberries	1 cup....7701
Blueberries	
Cultivated	1 cup....9019
Lowbrush	1 cup...13427
Cantaloupe	1 cup cubed.....499
Cherries	1 cup...4873
Cranberries	1 cup...8983
Dates	1/2 cup...3467
Figs, dried	1/2 cup...2537
Grapes	
Green	1 cup....1789
Red	1 cup...2016
Grapefruit	1/2....1904
Honeydew	1 cup diced.....410
Kiwifruit	1.....698
Mango	1 cup slices....1653
Nectarine	1....1019
Oranges	1...2540
Peaches	1....1826
Pears	
Green	1....3172
Red	1...2943
Pineapple	1 cup diced....1229
Plums	1.....4118
Prunes	1/2 cup.....7291
Raisins	1/2 cup....2490
Raspberries	1 cup...6058
Strawberries	1 cup...5938
Tangerines	1.....1361
Watermelon	1 cup diced.....216

*Vegetables are raw unless otherwise noted

Vegetables*	Total Antioxidant Capacity (TAC)
Artichoke hearts	1/2 cup cooked....3952
Asparagus	1/2 cup....2021
Beans, green	1/2 cup.....147
Beans, dried, cooked	
Black	1/2 cup....4181
Navy	1/2 cup....2573
Pinto	1/2 cup...11864
Red	1/2 cup...13727
Beets	1/2 cup...1886
Broccoli	1/2 cup.....700
Cabbage	
Green	1/2 cup.....476
Red	1/2 cup.....788
Carrots	1 medium......741
Cauliflower	1/2 cup.....324
Celery	1/2 cup.....344
Corn	1/2 cup frozen....428
Cucumber	1/2 cup.......74
Eggplant	1/2 cup....1039
Lettuces	
Butterhead	3 oz....1209
Green leaf	3 oz....1320
Iceberg	3 oz....383
Red leaf	3 oz.....1519
Onions	
Yellow	1/2 cup.....823
Red	1/2 cup......917
Peas, green	1/2 cup frozen.....480
Peppers, sweet	
Green	1.....664
Red	1....1072
Orange	1....1830
Yellow	1....1905
Potatoes	
Red	8 oz...2494
Russett	8 oz...2996
White	8 oz...2383
Radishes	1/2 cup sliced....1107
Spinach	3 oz....2249
Sweet Potato	5 oz....1173
Tomatoes	1 raw....415
	1/2 cup cooked.....552

An Apple A Day...

Exciting new research shows that apples contain potent disease-fighting antioxidants, similar to those in tea, chocolate and red wine.

Here's How Apples Improve Your Health

Help you breathe better. A large British study of 2,500 middle-aged men showed that those who ate five or more apples a week had nearly four times better breathing capacity and lung function than non-apple eaters – even among current and former smokers. Suspected reason: antioxidants in apples protected the lungs from atmospheric pollutants and irritants, including cigarette smoke.

Ward off cancer. High apple consumption cut the risk of lung cancer by 40 percent in a University of Hawaii study and by 60 percent in a recent Finnish study of 10,000 women and men. Further, Finns who ate the most "flavonoids" – a type of antioxidant concentrated in apples – were 20 percent less likely to develop any type of cancer. Investigators suggest that such antioxidants inhibit enzymes that activate carcinogens. New Cornell University test-tube studies even show that fresh apple extract suppresses growth of colon and liver cancer cells.

Prevent strokes. Those who ate the most apples were the least likely to suffer a blood clot-type stroke over a 28-year period, finds research by Finland's National Public Health Institute. Eating half an apple a day or more cut their risk of thrombotic stroke by about 40 percent, according

APPLE ADVICE

- Eat the skin. Antioxidants are more concentrated in the skin than in the pulp. Cornell tests show that apple extracts made with skin have twice the anti-cancer activity of extracts made with peeled apples.

- To remove possible pesticide residue, wash apple skins with a very diluted dishwashing detergent before eating, or buy organically grown apples, which have little or no residue.

- Store apples in a plastic bag in the refrigerator crisper, where they should keep as long as six weeks.

- Simply munch on raw apples or try them diced or thinly sliced in salads and cereals, chopped in tuna and chicken salad sandwiches or in rice, pilafs, stuffings and curries, grated into meatloaf or meatballs, sliced as scoops for dips.

to lead researcher Paul Knekt, Ph.D.

Fight heart attacks. In previous research, Knekt found that the women who ate the most apples were 43 percent less apt to die of heart disease than those who ate the least. Apple fiber, notably pectin, tends to lower bad LDL cholesterol. New research says apple antioxidants benefit vascular function and have anticoagulant activity similar to that of aspirin.

A recent analysis finds that some apples are super sources of one particularly promising flavonoid called procyanidins, also abundant in red wine and chocolate. In fact, University of California researchers at Davis, found that Red Delicious apples averaged 208 milligrams of procyanidins each, compared with 165 milligrams in a 1.3-ounce chocolate bar and 22 milligrams in 3½ ounces of red wine.

Leafy Greens for Lutein

Why are spinach, kale and other greens so good for you? One reason: they are packed with an antioxidant called lutein. It's a yellow pigment (covered by chlorophyll in green leaves) with newly discovered powers to fight disease. So far the evidence is impressive.

Here's How Lutein Boosts Health

Saves Aging Eyes: Lutein is most hailed as a possible way to protect eyes from macular degeneration, a leading cause of blindness in older people. A landmark Dutch study in men, showed that taking 10 milligrams of lutein ester daily for three months increased pigment thickness in an area of the retina known as the macula by 22 percent, presumably reducing its vulnerability to damage and loss of vision. Further, Harvard researchers found that eating 6 milligrams lutein per day in food (roughly ¼ cup cooked spinach) lowered the odds of macular degeneration by 43 percent. Remarkably, eating sautéed spinach four to seven times a week for three months even reversed some early signs of macular degeneration, according to Stuart Richer, Ph.D., at the North Chicago VA Medical Center.

Loading up on lutein also seems to reduce the odds of cataracts (opacity of the lens) by 20 to 50 percent, according to research.

Discourages Cancer: A recent study by Tufts University and Korean investigators revealed a dramatic 88 percent drop in breast cancer risk in women with the highest blood concentrations of lutein. University of Utah Medical School researchers found that the highest consumers of lutein (a mere 2.4 mg daily) were 17 percent less apt to develop colon cancer than those who ate the least (300 mcg). Generally, the more lutein consumed, the lower the risk.

How Much Do You Need?

The average American consumes about 1 milligram of lutein each day. Experts recommend at least 4 to 6 milligrams daily.

High lutein has also been linked to less prostate, lung, and ovarian cancers.

In animals, lutein even slowed the growth of breast tumors, and in test tubes, caused the death of cancer cells. Researchers speculate lutein switches off carcinogenic activity and boosts immune functioning.

Prevents Clogged Arteries: At the University of Southern California, professor James H. Dwyer measured the thickness of the carotid (neck) arteries of 480 middle-aged men and women. He repeated it a year and a half later. He discovered that those with the lowest blood lutein had the greatest progression of thickening – a sign of blood-vessel clogging throughout the body. In fact, the carotid thickening was four times greater in those with the lowest blood lutein than in those with the highest blood lutein. The conclusion: lutein helped prevent artery clogging.

A probable reason: lutein-bathed cells were less apt to promote bad LDL cholesterol's ability to stick to artery walls.

Delays Lung Aging: People who eat the most lutein have younger lungs, finds new research at the State University of New York of Buffalo. In fact, high lutein intake shaved one to two years off lung aging as indicated by standard lung function tests in 1616 men and women, aged 35 to 79. (High vitamin E intake also boosted breathing capacity.)

The new discovery could be lifesaving, because impaired lung function boosts the risk of death, said researchers. Lutein appears especially important for smokers, they added.

GET YOUR LUTEIN HERE

BEST FOOD SOURCES	PER ½ CUP
Kale, cooked	10.0 mg
Collard greens, cooked	7.7 mg
Spinach, raw	3.3 mg
Spinach, cooked	6.3 mg
Broccoli, raw	1.0 mg
Broccoli, cooked	1.7 mg
Brussels sprouts, cooked	1.7 mg
Yellow corn, cooked	1.2 mg

Egg yolks also have small amounts of lutein (about 200mcg per yolk) because chickens eat corn. However, egg lutein is particularly well absorbed by the body. Tufts University research showed that blood levels of lutein shot up 200 to 300 percent higher after eating egg yolks than after eating spinach!

Supplements: Lutein is also available as pills. Experts say from 4 to 10 mg daily may be needed to convey benefits shown in eye studies – the amount in ¼ to ½ cup cooked spinach.

Tomatoes–Red Hot Health Food

Until the 1800s, Americans considered the tomato a poisonous fruit, either rarely eaten or boiled for hours to destroy its "toxins." All that has radically changed in the last few years.

Now that scientists have discovered spectacular disease-fighting antioxidants, including the red pigment lycopene and an anti-clotting agent known as "P3 tomato factor," the tomato has become a hot health food to help prevent and even reverse disease.

Experts urge you to eat more tomatoes in any form – fresh or canned, raw or cooked, or processed in soups or as sauce, paste, juice or ketchup.

How Tomatoes Boost Health

Fight cancer. Researchers have known tomatoes might help prevent certain cancers. In a Harvard study, eating lycopene-rich tomato sauce two to four times weekly cut prostate cancer risk by 35 percent. The news is that lycopene may even *shrink* existing prostate tumors. Before surgery, one group of prostate cancer patients at the Barbara Ann Karmanos Cancer Institute in Detroit was given lycopene extract for three weeks; another group got a placebo. Tumors in the lycopene group were smaller and less likely to spread.

Protect lungs. Eating tomatoes helps shield lungs from bad air and cigarette smoke. In a University of North Carolina test, people were exposed to high levels of ozone, an air pollutant. Those who drank a 12-ounce can of tomato-rich V-8 juice daily in the three-week test showed 20 percent less DNA damage in lung cells than those not getting V-8. Other research suggests lycopene helps ward off lung cancer.

Combat heart disease. Tomatoes can make you less prone to clogged arteries and heart disease. Dramatic evidence from Finland shows that middle-aged men with low lycopene are three times more apt to suffer heart attacks or strokes and 18 percent more apt to have narrowed carotid (neck) arteries. Probable reasons: Tomatoes help detoxify bad LDL cholesterol, hindering plaque buildup. In one test, eating 60 milligrams of lycopene daily (the amount in 1 1/2 cups of tomato sauce or 2.2 pounds of fresh tomatoes) for three months reduced LDL cholesterol by 14 percent.

Also, an aspirin-like substance in the yellow jelly around tomato seeds helps thwart blood clots, according to Scottish research. The amount in only four tomatoes reduced clot-provoking blood stickiness by a surprising 72 percent.

Save Vision: Tomatoes may protect the eyes by deterring macular degeneration, a cause of vision loss in older people, suggests University of Maryland research that found high levels of lycopene in eye tissue.

Protect Skin: New German research shows that eating 1.3 ounces of tomato paste daily reduced sun-induced skin damage by 40 percent.

Slow Aging: Tomatoes are anti-aging nourishment for the brain. In a classic study at the University of Kentucky, elderly women with the highest lycopene blood levels remained the most mentally and physically active.

How to Get the Most Benefits

- **Eat at least five weekly servings of tomato-based foods.**
- **Eat tomatoes cooked, processed and prepared with a little olive oil.** Heating helps release lycopene, and you get the most lycopene in concentrated, processed products such as tomato paste

and sauce, canned tomatoes, juice, soup and ketchup. In new tests at Ohio State University, over a two-week period, blood lycopene was raised 192 percent by a daily serving of tomato sauce, 122 percent by tomato soup and 92 percent by V-8 juice. Other research shows that adding olive oil to tomatoes increases lycopene absorption.

- **Eat a variety.** Lycopene isn't the sole tomato power. For example, tomato soup has more antioxidant activity than can be attributed to lycopene alone, meaning it contains other antioxidants. Raw tomatoes are lower in lycopene, but still may be good at combating blood clots.

Spinach - A Health Powerhouse

Spinach is packed with vitamins, minerals and antioxidants that protect you all your life.

Scientists constantly discover new reasons to eat spinach:

- Eating cooked spinach more than twice a week cuts the need for cataract eye surgery in men by half, according to new Harvard University research. And including at least two servings a week in your diet cuts the odds of macular degeneration (a leading cause of blindness) in half, says the National Eye Institute.
- Feeding spinach to laboratory animals helped prevent and reverse memory loss, report Tufts University investigators.
- People who eat at least one serving of greens, including spinach, each week are

> "Eat spinach raw. Eat it cooked. Eat it any way you can find to eat it. I call it the king of vegetables."
>
> — *Steven Pratt, ophthalmologist, Scripps Clinic in La Jolla, California.*

20 percent less likely to develop colon cancer, according to Italian research.
- And in a large-scale Harvard study, those same leafy greens were singled out as most protective against stroke.
- Because it's high in vitamin K, spinach also helps build stronger bones, lowering the risk of hip fracture from osteoporosis as much as 30 percent, suggests a joint Harvard-Tufts study.

Spinach's secret weapons: the antioxidants beta and alpha carotene, lutein and zeaxanthin as well as potassium, magnesium, vitamin K and particularly all-important folic acid. Spinach is the richest plant source of folic acid, which helps prevent serious birth defects and suppresses homocysteine, a blood factor tied to higher rates of heart disease, strokes, depression and Alzheimer's. One half-cup of cooked spinach provides two-thirds of the daily value for folic acid.

One downside: Spinach is rich in oxalic acid, which may contribute to kidney stones in some susceptible people.

Tip: The disease-fighting antioxidants in spinach are better absorbed from cooked spinach with a little added fat, such as olive or canola oil.

Brain-Boosting Berries

Imagine! Eating blueberries (also strawberries and spinach) may help save and rejuvenate your aging brain, says James Joseph, Ph.D., Tufts University. That's what he found when he fed aged laboratory animals modest amounts of berries and spinach. "They became smarter and younger," he says.

How much did they get? The human equivalent of a pint of strawberries or a large spinach salad or a cup of blueberries every day. The results were startling.

In one test, Joseph took old rats – between 65 and 70 years old in human terms – with diminished memory, motor coordination and balance. All the rats fed blueberries, spinach or strawberries regained short-term memory. In other words, their memory had returned to being "young" or "middle-aged" again. Blueberries proved most potent in rejuvenating brain functions.

Blueberries, but not strawberries and spinach, also reversed the age-related loss of motor coordination and balance in the old animals, which Dr. Joseph called amazing. "I know of no drug that could do the same thing," he says. Examinations revealed that the blueberries apparently had partially repaired the age-induced damage to brain cells, accounting for the rejuvenation.

A slew of evidence confirms the powers of blueberries. Elderly rats fed blueberry extract beat younger rats on memory tests at the University of Houston. In Canadian studies, feeding lab animals blueberries reduced stroke damage.

In a test of senior citizens, those who ate a cup of blueberries a day for a month had faster reaction times and made fewer errors on a computer test, according to a study reported at the 2003 annual conference of the American Aging Association. The improvement was enough to prevent the expected decline in reaction speed due to a year or two of aging, concluded researchers.

Spice Up Your Health!

Spices, herbs and peppers are more than seasonings to please your palate. Although we eat them in small doses, they can have a major impact on our health.

Herbs and spices act as antioxidants, antibiotics, anti-inflammatory agents, blood thinners, stomach-soothers, blood-sugar regulators, brain-cell protectors, even cancer fighters and calorie burners.

Strongest Antioxidants, beginning with the most potent: Oregano, thyme, sage, cumin, rosemary, saffron, turmeric, nutmeg, ginger, cardamom, coriander (cilantro), basil and tarragon. A test at the University of California-Davis declares thyme equal to vitamin E in antioxidant power.

Strongest Antibiotics (beginning with the most effective): Here are the most ferocious killers of 30 different bacterial species, according to Cornell University tests – in order : onion, garlic, allspice, oregano, thyme, tarragon, cumin, cloves, bay leaf, capsicum pepper (cayenne), rosemary, marjoram, mustard, mint, sage, coriander, dill, basil, parsley, black and white pepper, ginger.

Best Health Boosters

Oregano: "No wonder oregano has been used since antiquity to fight infections," says Harry Preuss, M.D, George Washington University. He recently found oregano oil as effective as the common antibiotic drug, vancomycin, in treating staph infections in mice. The oregano also wiped out an infectious fungus, reduced blood pressure and improved blood sugar and insulin sensitivity in diabetic rats.

Turmeric: The yellow spice turmeric, a constituent of curry powder, is rich in curcumin, a potent antioxidant that may help stifle cancer. In test tubes, 80 percent of malignant prostate cells exposed to curcumin died. Feeding mice curcumin slowed the growth of implanted human prostate cancer cells, and may do the same to breast and colon cancer cells.

Moreover, curcumin's anti-inflammatory activity reduces the swelling of arthritis and progressive brain damage in animals. Eating food laced with low doses of curcumin slashed Alzheimer's-like plaque in the brains of mice by 50 percent, says UCLA research. Researchers suspect curcumin in curry powder may be one reason the population of India has low rates of Alzheimer's disease.

Ginger: As a natural anti-inflammatory, ginger may help relieve inflammation in arthritis, heart disease, stroke, Alzheimer's, and possibly cancer. Ginger compounds (gingerols) reduce pain in animals and act as Cox-2 inhibitors, similar to the antiarthritis drug, Celebrex, according to Australian scientists at Sydney University. Further, gingerols thin the blood "just like aspirin," the Aussies noted, confirming that ginger is a mild anticoagulant. When given ginger for six weeks, arthritis patients at the University of Miami had less knee pain than those not getting ginger. Ginger is also a well-established suppressor of nausea.

Cinnamon: Adding a little cinnamon to food helps prevent spikes in blood sugar, says Richard Anderson, Ph.D, US Department of Agriculture. "Cinnamon can help normalize blood sugar by making insulin more sensitive and efficient," he finds. He recently isolated cinnamon's most active ingredient – methylhydroxy chalcone polymer (MHCP). The cinnamon compound increased the processing of blood sugar by about 2000 percent or 20-fold in test tube studies. Cloves, turmeric and bay leaves also energize insulin, but are much weaker. Using cinnamon could be especially important for type 2 diabetics, says Dr. Anderson, and could help prevent onset of such diabetes. In animals, low steady insulin levels are a sign of slower aging and greater longevity.

> **TIP:**
> When peppers get too hot, try a chaser of yogurt, beer, whole milk or ice cream. They are better than water or soft drinks at putting out fiery aftertastes.

Hot Chile Peppers: If you have asthma, emphysema, chronic bronchitis, sinusitis, congestion from a cold or the flu, or other breathing problems, eat hot peppers and hot sauce, advises Irwin Ziment, M.D., professor of medicine at UCLA. He says hot peppers work like expectorants to trigger a flash flood of fluids in the air passages, breaking up mucus, flushing out the sinuses and washing away irritants. "When you're congested," Ziment says, "it's better to eat salsa than to suck on a menthol cough drop."

Hot peppers can also suppress appetite and burn off extra calories. In a British study, eating three-fifths of a teaspoon of hot chile sauce increased average metabolism 25 percent, burning off 45 calories in the next three hours. Canadian subjects given an appetizer with hot sauce ate 200 fewer calories later than men not given hot sauce. Incidentally, chile peppers do not damage normal stomachs, or cause ulcers or heartburn, but they can worsen existing heartburn.

Garlic: An ancient folk medicine, garlic has antibacterial, antiviral, anticancer, anti-blood clotting, anti-inflammatory, cholesterol-reducing, immune-boosting and decongestive properties, according to modern research. Strongest evidence exists for its anticancer activity. A recent study of 42,000 older women in Iowa, for example, found that those who ate garlic more than once a week were about half as apt to develop colon cancer as women who never ate garlic. In test tube studies, a specific garlic compound suppressed the growth of prostate cancer cells by about 25 percent, indicating garlic might help block cancer spread.

Garlic may kill viruses responsible for colds and flu, according to tests. UCLA's Dr. Ziment recommends garlic as a remedy for congestion from a flu or cold. He notes that garlic's alliin, which gives garlic its flavor, behaves like a decongestant, mimicking a drug widely used to break up mucus in the lungs. Other studies suggest garlic revs up immune functioning by stimulating the potency of infection-fighting T cells.

Raw or cooked? For antibacterial or antiviral effect, raw garlic is best. However, both raw and cooked garlic seems to have cardiovascular, decongestive and anticancer benefits.

Too much? High doses of raw garlic (usually more than three cloves a day) have caused gas, bloating, diarrhea and fever in some persons. Cooked garlic is gentler on the stomach.

GO EASY ON SALT

Americans eat two or three times more sodium than is good for us. Here's how to cut back:

- Buy fresh, plain frozen or canned "no-salt added" vegetables. Canned corn has 100 times more sodium than frozen. Regular canned tomatoes have ten times more sodium than "no-salt added" canned tomatoes. Look for "no-salt added" canned beans at health food stores and some supermarkets.

- Restrict cured meats (bacon, ham), foods packed in brine (pickles, olives,sauerkraut), condiments (MSG, soy sauce, mustard, catsup, barbecue and chili sauce.)

- Use spices instead of salt to flavor foods.

- Drain and rinse canned foods, such as tuna and beans to remove some sodium.

- Cook rice, pasta, hot cereals, beans and other vegetables without salt.

- Eat fewer frozen dinners and pizzas, packaged mixes, canned soups or broths and salad dressings — often loaded with sodium. Or look for low-sodium versions.

Nuts
The New Superfood

Not long ago, nuts were dismissed as "fattening snacks." Today, experts urge you to eat nuts to save your heart, reduce diabetes, ward off cancer, lose weight and perhaps fend off Parkinson's disease, and live longer. Nuts are definitely one of the primary ingredients of a healthy diet.

"Nuts are excellent substitutes for meat, cheese and other fatty foods, and satisfy the craving for fat," says Gene Spiller, Ph.D., director of the Health Research and Studies Center in Los Altos, California. Sure, nuts contain a significant amount of fat, but it's mostly the good monounsaturated type that discourages disease. Walnuts also contain high levels of healthy omega-3 fats.

Nuts are also packed with fiber, vitamins and minerals, including calcium, folate, potassium, magnesium, vitamin E and cancer-fighting antioxidants such as quercetin and kaempferol. Nuts are rich in arginine, an amino acid that relaxes blood vessels, helping lower blood pressure and deter blood clots. Brazil nuts are also the richest source of selenium, thought to help improve mood and prevent certain cancers.

Here's How Nuts Keep You Healthy

Reduce heart disease. Consistently, studies find that nut-eaters are from 30 to 50 percent less apt to develop or die of heart disease. In a pioneering study at Loma Linda University, eating two ounces of nuts four or five times a week slashed heart attack risk 50 percent. A large Harvard study found heart attacks were one-third less likely among women who ate five ounces of nuts weekly compared with women who ate nuts once a month. In fact, a diet high in fatty peanuts and peanut butter helps hearts and improves cholesterol more than a typical low-fat regimen, says Penn State research.

The Food and Drug Administration now agrees that eating an ounce and a half of nuts (about one-third cup) a day, including almonds, hazelnuts, pecans, pistachios, walnuts and peanuts, as part of a low animal fat diet, may reduce heart disease.

Lower cholesterol: In several studies, eating almonds, walnuts or macadamia nuts (two to three ounces a day) depressed bad type LDL cholesterol by up to 29 percent, and in some cases raised good HDL cholesterol by up to eight percent. In Loma Linda University research, walnuts even enhance the cholesterol-lowering power of a Mediterranean diet. Eating eight to 11 walnuts daily instead of other fats, such as olive oil, further lowered bad cholesterol about 6 percent. This reduced heart disease risk 11 per cent. A daily ounce of almonds was part of a low-fat Canadian diet that reduced cholesterol as effectively as statin drugs (Lipitor) did.

Combat diabetes: A long-term Harvard study of 83,000 women nurses, ages 34 to 59, found that nuts, including peanuts, significantly lower the risk of developing type 2 diabetes. Women who ate an ounce of nuts more than five times a week were nearly 30 percent less apt to have diabetes as those who never ate nuts or less than an ounce a week, regardless of weight or other risk factors for diabetes.

Further, women who ate peanut butter five times or more a week (equal to five ounces of peanuts) had a 20 percent lower risk of diabetes than women who rarely or never ate peanut butter.

Reduce cancer risk. Nuts may lower the risk of colon, stomach and prostate cancers. In India, eating cashews is linked to less colon cancer, says Bandaru Reddy of the American Health Foundation. Canadian research suggests eating nuts and legumes can reduce the risk of prostate cancer 30 percent. Harvard investigators say eating nuts, seeds and beans can reduce risk of endometrial cancer.

Prevent Parkinson's disease: In a first-of-its-kind finding, Harvard researchers analyzing the diets of large groups of doctors and female nurses in its long-term ongoing studies, found that nuts may protect against Parkinson's disease. Individuals who ate an ounce of nuts more than five times a week, compared with less than once a month, had a surprising 43 per cent lower risk of developing Parkinson's disease.

Promote weight loss. Contrary to popular opinion, people who eat nuts are not fatter than those who don't. And studies show nut-eaters are apt to lose weight and keep it off. Purdue University research found peanut butter dampened the appetite, staving off hunger for two-and-a-half hours compared with a mere half-hour for snacks such as rice cakes. In a study at Boston's Brigham and Women's Hospital, dieters on equal calories lost more weight on a diet high in monounsaturated fat, including nuts, peanuts and peanut butter, than on a very low-fat diet and kept it off longer. After 18 months, high-fat nut eaters had lost nine pounds; low-fat dieters gained more than six pounds.

Possible reasons: Nuts suppress hunger and curb intake of other foods. Further, the fat in nuts is not totally absorbed. Peanuts have an extremely low glycemic index, meaning they don't spike blood sugar that leads to hunger and weight gain.

NUTTY ANTIOXIDANTS

TOTAL ANTIOXIDANT CAPACITY PER OUNCE

1.	Pecans	5095
2.	Walnuts	3846
3.	Hazelnuts	2739
4.	Pistachios	2267
5.	Almonds	1265
6.	Peanuts	899
7.	Cashews	567
8.	Macadamias	481
9.	Brazil nuts	403
10.	Pine nuts	204

Sweet News About Chocolate

Have you heard? Experts are saying chocolate can be good for your heart. Surprising new research finds that chocolate contains health-promoting chemicals, similar to those in red wine, tea and fruits and vegetables.

Even the prestigious *New England Journal of Medicine's* "Heart Watch" newsletter says "a sizeable chunk of research" suggests that cocoa bean compounds have modest "beneficial effects on specific factors linked to heart disease." The scientific *Journal of Nutrition* recently devoted an entire issue to an investigation of chocolate's "medicinal benefits."

Here Are the Ways Chocolate Guards Health

Provides antioxidants galore: Chocolate is rich in cell-protecting antioxidants. An ounce-and-a-half of milk chocolate typically has 400 milligrams of antioxidants, about the same as a glass of red wine, reports chemistry professor Joe A. Vinson, of the University of Scranton (Pennsylvania). Dark chocolate has twice as much. White chocolate has none. Further, antioxidant activity jumped 31 percent in the blood of subjects two hours after eating 2.8 ounces of M&M's semisweet chocolate baking bits, according to research at the University of California, Davis. In another Italian study, eating dark chocolate boosted antioxidant blood levels more than milk chocolate did. Clearly, dark chocolate delivers the most antioxidants and greatest benefits.

Fights cholesterol: Antioxidants in chocolate help block chemical changes in bad LDL cholesterol that lead to clogged arteries. In fact, Vinson found chocolate's antioxidants more potent in detoxifying LDLs than vitamin C. And new research by Penny Kris-Etherton at Pennsylvania State University, shows that diets rich in dark chocolate or cocoa powder raise good HDL cholesterol. Previously, she found that eating a milk chocolate bar every day for a month (in place of another high carbo snack) did not raise bad LDL cholesterol in men.

Blocks blood clots: Chocolate's antioxidants act like aspirin to reduce blood platelet stickiness and thus clots that trigger heart attacks and strokes. In a recent study, 30 subjects drank either plain water, a caffeine drink or a cocoa beverage containing one-and-a-half times the antioxidants in a typical eight-ounce cup of hot cocoa. The cocoa significantly delayed blood clotting time.

Relaxes blood vessels: Good vascular function – how well blood vessels relax –

helps prevent heart disease, particularly high blood pressure and artery clogging. Chocolate's antioxidants called procyanidins relax blood vessels by increasing concentrations of the chemical, nitric oxide, according to studies at the University of California, Davis School of Medicine. UC research also shows that chocolate's antioxidants help suppress inflammatory processes, now recognized as a prime villain in cardiovascular disease.

Reduces blood pressure: When German subjects with mild high blood pressure ate a three-ounce dark chocolate bar daily for two weeks, their blood pressure sank. Systolic pressure (upper number) dropped an average 5.1 mm Hg and diastolic fell 1.9 mm Hg. Experts said the reduction was very similar to that from a low-salt diet.

Questioning Chocolate's Dark Side

Won't chocolate make you fat? Since chocolate is packed with fat and sugar, overindulging is bound to put on pounds. But chocolate is not a prime cause of obesity, according to worldwide studies. The Swiss, for example, eat twice as much chocolate per person as Americans – about 22 pounds a year – but still have one of the lowest rates of obesity.

Isn't chocolate full of artery-clogging fat? About 60 percent of chocolate's fat is saturated – and a typical chocolate bar contains 8 grams of saturated fat, so bingeing on chocolate drives up saturated fat intake. But moderate amounts of chocolate do not appear to be harmful. Extensive Harvard research found that women who ate chocolate bars three to four times a week were no more likely to have heart disease than women who rarely ate chocolate.

Isn't the sugar in chocolate unhealthy? In excess, yes. However, a chocolate bar's glycemic index – the ability to drive up blood sugar – is lower than that of sugary cereals and bagels.

What about chocolate's caffeine? A dark chocolate bar's 10 to 30 milligrams of caffeine is modest compared with the 100 milligrams in a cup of coffee.

> **TIP:**
> To get the most benefits, consume dark chocolate, which has more antioxidants than milk chocolate. White chocolate has none.

> **BOTTOM LINE:**
> Chocolate's newly discovered health benefits make it more than just an empty calorie junk food. But nobody is saying it's OK to eat five to nine chocolate bars a day instead of apples and carrots. Chocolate is still a high-fat, sugary occasional indulgence, not an everyday healthy staple like fruits and vegetables.

Cancer-Proof Your Barbecue
And Other Meaty Advice

There's mounting evidence that eating meat can have serious health consequences. Heavy meat-eaters tend to have more heart disease, cancer and other chronic diseases and a shorter life expectancy. However, you can dramatically reduce the danger by eating less red meat (substituting poultry, fish and other protein sources) and cooking meat in ways that minimize formation of carcinogens.

The disturbing facts: Increasing evidence incriminates red meat (beef, pork, veal, lamb) as a cause of cancer. "Eating substantial amounts of red meat may increase the risk of colorectal, pancreatic, breast, prostate and renal cancer," the National Cancer Institute recently declared. Further, frying and grilling/barbecuing red meat worsens the hazard.

Studies Uncover Cancer Risk

Men and women who ate the most red meat (average three ounces daily), especially well-done and/or fried, doubled their risk of colon cancer compared with those who ate the least (less than half an ounce daily), says a new study by the National Institute of Environmental Health Sciences. Breast cancer risk was twice as high in postmenopausal women who ate three ounces or more of red meat a day compared with women who consumed an ounce or less daily, according to a new

study at the Portland (Oregon) VA Medical Center. Odds of breast cancer jumped 85 percent in premenopausal women who ate the most red meat compared to those eating the least, says a recent German study. Vanderbilt University investigators determined that women who ate the most deep-fried, well-done meat had nearly twice the odds of developing breast cancer as those who ate the least.

The odds of pancreatic cancer doubled in people who ate the most grilled or barbecued red meat (ranging from three to 21 ounces a week) compared to non-red meat eaters, finds a recent University of Minnesota study.

High-Heat Hazards

Much of the danger depends on how meat is cooked. Heat reacts with a protein in meat muscle (as well as in poultry and fish to a lesser degree) to form cancer-promoting chemicals called heterocyclic amines (HCAs). The higher and more prolonged the heat, as in grilling and frying, the greater the amounts of HCAs formed. Moreover, the carcinogenic HCAs are embedded deep in the meat, so you can't scrape them off the surface as you can the char from barbecue. Poultry and fish, although they too, may contain HCAs, do not appear to be nearly as dangerous as red meat.

Ways to Reduce the Threat

Substitute fish or poultry for red meat. Fish is safest, tests show, and may even discourage breast cancer risk. Women who ate fish three or more times weekly had a 30 percent lower breast cancer risk than women who ate fish once a week in the recent study at Portland (Oregon) VA Medical Center. In another study, eating chicken baked, broiled or barbecued did not raise colon cancer risk. However, pan-frying chicken boosted odds 50 percent. You can also substitute turkey, chicken or veggie burgers for beef burgers.

Cook smart: You can dramatically reduce dangerous HCAs by microwaving, poaching, stewing and roasting meat, poultry and fish. Prolonged cooking at high temperature, such as barbecuing and frying burgers, chicken and chops well-done, produces the most HCAs. Consistently eating crispy bacon and beef steak very well done, instead of rare or medium, boosted women's breast cancer risk nearly five times in a University of Minnesota study.

Best way to cook meat: in the oven and simmering on the top of the stove – and best of all, in the microwave where internal temperatures are no more than that of boiling water. Contrary to popular opinion, microwaving is not a high temperature way of cooking. Important: hamburgers must be cooked well done to kill infectious agents, such as E coli. See barbecue tips for reducing the hazards in hamburgers on pages 40-41.

Eat less red meat: Use smaller portions as in stews, casseroles, stir-frys, not as the centerpiece of a meal.

Avoid or restrict nitrite-cured meats: This includes ham, bacon, hot dogs and cold cuts. Nitrite can react with other chemicals in the intestinal tract to form nitrosamines, a potent family of carcinogens, linked to higher rates of stomach, pancreatic and brain cancer and leukemia. Always microwave bacon; it reduces nitrosamines by about 90 percent.

HCA Questions:

Is fish safer? In one study fried fish had only 20 percent as many HCAs as fried chicken and beef. It's safest to poach, bake or microwave fish.

Is it okay to grill vegetables? Grilling vegetables at high heat does not form HCAs, says researcher James Felton because they do not contain the meat protein that produces HCAs.

What about roast turkey and meat loaf? There's little hazard from HCAs because of the usually low oven temperature of 350 degrees or so. Also, it's unlikely turkey gravy made from such drippings are high in HCAs.

TEN WAYS TO CANCER-PROOF YOUR BARBECUE

Scientists have come up with ingenious ways to dramatically reduce the formation of carcinogens in grilled meat. Here are ten tested ways to make your barbecue safer:

Flip burgers often. Turning burgers once a minute and cooking over lower heat reduces formation of cancer-causing HCAs and kills potentially deadly E. coli bacteria, finds a new study at Lawrence Livermore National Laboratory in California. Important: Use a meat thermometer to make sure a burger's internal temperature reaches 160º Fahrenheit, needed to deactivate E. coli. Just because meat is brown doesn't mean it's thoroughly cooked.

Use the right marinade. Slash HCAs by marinating raw meat in a thin, very liquid sauce for at least 10 minutes, or more to taste. The Cancer Research Center of Hawaii found that a teriyaki marinade reduced HCAs 67 percent; a turmeric-garlic sauce, 50 percent. (Recipes on page 194). The key is to use a watery sauce: when a thick, concentrated commercial barbecue sauce was used, it actually tripled HCAs. So dilute thick sauces.

Microwave first. Partially cook burgers, poultry, ribs and fish in a microwave oven before grilling, and be sure to discard the juices. Microwaving a hamburger a couple of minutes or a batch of ribs and chicken 5 to 15 minutes eliminates 90 percent of HCAs, says James Felton, Ph.D., at Lawrence Livermore Lab. Important: Be sure to drain off the microwave meat juices that contain the raw material for formation of HCAs. Don't use them to make gravy or sauces.

Add soy protein. Mix half a cup of textured soy protein into a pound of ground meat (beef, pork, veal, lamb, turkey, chicken) before grilling. This cuts 95 percent of the expected HCAs in burgers without appreciably affecting the taste, according to tests by John Weisburger, Ph.D., at the American Health Foundation.

Enhance with E. Adding vitamin E to raw ground meat hinders HCAs, says J. Ian Gray, Ph.D., of Michigan State University. His tests showed that 120 milligrams of vitamin E powder mixed into or sprinkled on 3.5-ounce patties can reduce HCA formation as much as 72 percent. Just crack open a capsule of powdered vitamin E.

Try a "fruit burger." Mixing a pound of ground meat with a cup of ground, dried tart cherries before grilling suppresses 90 percent of HCA formation, according to research at Michigan State. A possible reason: Cherries are high in HCA-blocking antioxidants. Researchers say other deep-colored fruits rich in antioxidants (red grapes blueberries, plums) should work, too. (see recipe for Blueberry Burger, page 192).

Add garlic and herbs. In tests, garlic, rosemary and sage reduced HCAs, Gray says. Mix them into burgers, use them in marinades or just eat them in a meal with grilled meat. Antioxidants in citrus fruits also block HCAs.

Beware well-done. The longer meat is cooked at high temperatures (grilling and frying) the more HCAs are produced. Cooking steaks very well-done, compared to simply well-done, doubles HCAs. To minimize HCAs, grill beefsteaks and lamb rare or medium-rare. But always cook burgers, pork and poultry well-done to avoid food poisoning. Do not eat the charred skin of barbecued meat, poultry or fish; it contains carcinogens.

Wash down barbecued food with tea. Chemicals in black and green tea help detoxify HCAs, Weisburger says. He recommends drinking hot or iced tea brewed from bags or loose tea (not bottled teas or powdered instant teas) regularly – and especially with barbecue. Or marinate meat, poultry and fish in concentrated tea (let a tea bag steep in ¼ cup hot water for 5 minutes).

Skip the meat – grill "green." Fruits and vegetables don't contain the animal protein needed to make HCAs. Pineapple and peppers are great grilled. Also, eating antioxidant-packed fruits, vegetables and green salads along with barbecued meat lessens the cancer hazard.

Tea
The Healthiest Drink

It's time to pay serious attention to tea.

New research reveals some remarkable new health properties of both black and green tea. Recent studies in leading medical journals have declared tea a potential heart-tonic, fat-buster, brain booster, cancer blocker, cavity-fighter, sight-saver, immune-stimulant, arthritis-soother, anti-viral agent, cholesterol-suppressor and detoxifier. Not bad for a lowly shrub soaked in a little hot water.

"Tea is beating all scientific expectations as the most potent health beverage ever," says researcher John Weisburger, of the American Health Foundation. "The many ways tea can promote health is truly astonishing."

The bottom line is you should drink tea – black tea, green tea, hot or iced – several cups a day, advises Weisburger.

Here's How Tea Boosts Health

Saves arteries: Drinking black tea helps prevent deadly artery clogging and reverses poor arterial functioning that can trigger heart attacks and strokes, according to two major new studies. In a large ten-year Dutch study, men who consumed the amount of specific antioxidants called "catechins" in three cups of black tea a day were 50 percent less apt to die of ischemic heart disease, caused by narrowed clogged arteries, than men consuming the catechins in about half a cup of tea a day.

In another recent test, Joseph Vita, M.D. professor of medicine at Boston University School of Medicine, had heart patients drink either four cups of black tea daily or plain water for a month. Remarkably, impaired blood vessel functioning, a risk factor for heart attack and strokes, improved about 50 percent in the tea drinkers!

Moreover, a recent U.S. Department of Agriculture study found that drinking five cups of black tea daily (30 fluid ounces or slightly less than a quart) reduced bad LDL cholesterol by 11 percent within three weeks!

Inhibits cancer growth: Drinking tea has long been tied to a lower risk of certain cancers, notably, stomach, colon and breast, although the connection is not proven. Now lab studies find that tea chemicals may actually stop cancer growth. Rutgers University researchers showed that a compound in black tea called (TF-2) caused colorectal cancer cells to commit suicide; normal colon cells were unaffected. "The effect is quite dramatic," said Rutgers professor Kuang Yu Chen, who speculates the tea chemical might one day be made into an anti-cancer drug.

Tames inflammation: Chemicals in both black and green tea have anti-inflammatory activity that may combat arthritis. Case Western Reserve researchers gave arthritis-prone mice either green tea or water. The human equivalent of four cups of green tea daily cut the mice's risk of developing arthritis in half. Also intriguing, the newly discovered anti-cancer black tea compound TF-2 suppresses the Cox 2 gene that triggers inflammation, say Rutgers researchers. "That's the same way two popular new drugs (Vioxx and Celebrex) work to relieve arthritis," they point out. Investigators at UCLA report that drinking green tea reduced by half the risk of chronic stomach inflammation (gastritis), a prelude to stomach cancer, in a study of 600 Chinese men and women.

Wipes out viruses: Previous tests prove tea can neutralize a variety of germs, including some that cause diarrhea, pneumonia, cystitis and skin infections. New research by Milton Schiffenbauer of Pace University in New York finds that black and green tea inactivates viruses, including herpes. He says when you drink tea, chances are good you wipe out viruses in your mouth. Flu viruses, too? Possibly. A recent Japanese study did show that gargling with black tea boosted immunity to influenza. Recent Harvard research indicated that tea chemicals stimulated gamma-delta T-cells that bolster immune defenses against bacteria and viruses.

Burns off calories: Most surprising, green tea's antioxidant, EGCG stimulates the body to burn energy, notably fat. In short, it converts flab to heat, getting rid

TEA TIPS

- Steep tea leaves in hot water for three to five minutes to release antioxidants. Bags are as good as loose tea.

- Herbal teas are not "real tea," known as "Camellia sinensis," and do not have the same health properties.

- Tea with caffeine has much more antioxidant activity than decaffeinated tea.

- Adding lemon, sugar, and milk to brewed tea does not substantially reduce its benefits.

- Don't give excessive amounts of tea to babies and children. Tea tends to "chelate" iron, removing it from the body, which may help combat chronic diseases, such as heart disease and cancer in adults. However, excessive tea has caused anemia in children.

- Don't drink bottled, instant and herbal teas to get antioxidants. Tests show they contain little or none. Iced tea is okay and has antioxidants if it's made from real tea bags or loose tea.

of calories. So found Abdul G. Dulloo of the University of Fribourg in Switzerland. He gave men three capsules daily containing 270 mg EGCG – the amount in two to three cups of green tea. It caused them to burn four percent more energy – about 80 additional calories a day. Further, green tea did not increase heart rate and the extra calorie-burning was not due to caffeine.

And still more: Researchers at McGill University in Canada blocked cavities in mice by giving them tea to drink instead of water. Eye researchers in India retarded progression of cataracts in rats by feeding them green or black tea extract. Israeli scientists blocked Parkinson's-like brain damage in mice by giving them green tea extract or pure ECGC, the tea's primary antioxidant.

THE SPECIAL MAGIC OF GREEN TEA

Although it's health-smart to drink any real brewed tea, including popular black tea, green tea appears superior, say recent studies. Commercial green teas average about twice the antioxidant activity as black teas, according to a new UCLA analyses. So you may have to drink twice as much black as green tea for similar benefits.

Moreover, green tea has higher concentrations of potent catechin antioxidants, mainly one called epigallo-catechin-gallate (EGCG). Here are some specific new findings that make green tea a high priority:

- Consuming the EGCG in two or three cups of green tea helped block the spread of human lung cancer cells in Japanese tests.
- The EGCG in three cups of green tea normalized vascular dysfunction (a condition that can trigger heart attacks) in patients with heart disease, says Boston University research.
- EGCG destroyed leukemia cells by disrupting their survival communication network in a groundbreaking discovery at the Mayo Clinic.
- EGCG blocked expected alcohol-induced liver damage in rats, including fat accumulation, inflammation and necrosis (death) of liver cells in University of North Carolina tests.
- EGCG inhibited growth of 80 percent of human breast cancer cells without damaging normal cells, report University of Alabama scientists.
- EGCG interfered with angiogenesis, formation of blood vessels that supply food to cancer cells, thus, starving the cancer, in Tufts University studies
- Green tea extract strongly inhibited spread of infection by Helicobacter pylori bacteria that cause gastrointestinal ulcers and possibly stomach cancer in animals, find Japanese researchers.

PART 2:

Vitamin Advice From the Experts

The Multivitamin Mineral Pill
Why Everybody Needs One

Vitamin/mineral supplements give your body a "tune-up" and are insurance against health breakdown, says biochemist Bruce Ames, who wants everybody in the world to take a multivitamin/mineral pill. Ames, age 74, is a world-renowned researcher on antioxidants and nutrients at the University of California at Berkeley and Children's Hospital of Oakland Research Institute. Because of poor diets, he says, widespread micronutrient deficiencies could condemn millions of Americans to poor health and substandard mental achievement.

In groundbreaking research, Ames and his group discovered a frightening picture of what happens to cells deprived of proper amounts of micronutrients. Their DNA (genetic material) and energy producing centers (mitochondria) are damaged. This damage could lead to cancer, brain cell decay and cognitive dysfunction, accelerated aging and degenerative diseases such as Alzheimer's and Parkinson's. Most astonishing, the nutrient-deprived cells look like they were exposed to radiation – as from atomic bomb fallout and X-rays – well documented as a cause of cancer. In short, being vitamin and mineral deficient is like being irradiated – constantly.

Who should worry? More than half of Americans, notably the young, the poor, the elderly and the obese, may have at least one vitamin/mineral deficiency that can mimic radiation damage, says Ames. Particularly worrisome: low levels of folic acid, zinc, B12, B6 and iron (in premenopausal women.) The developing fetus and growing children are especially vulnerable. Note: in post-menopausal women and men age 18 and over, too much iron can accelerate aging and promote heart disease and cancer. Men and postmenopausal women should not take iron supplements, unless a doctor recommends or prescribes them.

Why Multivitamins Are Good for You

Heart Disease: In a recent Swedish study, men who took multivitamins had a 20 percent lower risk of heart attacks, and women a 35 percent lower risk than those not taking supplements.

Infections: Taking multivitamins for a year boosted immune functioning and cut infections, such as the flu, 40 percent in diabetics and 50 percent in the elderly, compared with taking a placebo, according to tests at the University of North Carolina and Memorial University of Newfoundland.

Cancer: Harvard studies show that taking multivitamins containing folic acid cut the risk of colon cancer 50 percent in women with a family history of the disease.

Cataracts: Taking a multivitamin pill for more than ten years slashed the risk of cataracts by 60 percent. So finds a study of 3,089 people, ages 43 to 86, by ophthalmologists at the University of Wisconsin-Madison.

Kids' IQ: Ten out of 13 studies show that giving children multivitamin/mineral pills raised their nonverbal IQ scores as much as 30 percent, reports British psychologist David Benton, University of Wales Swansea. Benton estimates that one-third to one-half of all children have mild, unsuspected nutritional deficiencies that can be corrected by a multivitamin.

Even the conservative medical establishment now agrees that taking vitamins is essential. Writing in the *Journal of the American Medical Association*, two Harvard researchers advise all adult Americans to take a multivitamin supplement. They cite 30 years of studies showing the connection between low vitamin intake and increased risk of chronic diseases, such as cancer and heart disease.

Take Antioxidants To Stay Young

Taking a low-dose multivitamin/mineral pill that provides 100 percent of the recommended daily allowances can fill in nutrient gaps, significantly boosting health. But these doses are not powerful enough to provide "optimal" protection for most people, especially as they grow older, according to compelling research.

As you age, you need potent antioxidants that low-dose multivitamins lack. Antioxidants help neutralize cellular enemies called free radical chemicals that are considered a primary cause of accelerated aging and chronic disease. Start taking antioxidant supplements when you're young and healthy to stay that way, say leading researchers.

Chronic conditions like cancer and cardiovascular disease take decades to develop. So do wrinkles and fuzzy brains. That's why one of the world's leading authorities on antioxidants says no adult is too young to start taking these popular supplements.

After decades of research, Lester Packer, Ph.D., a molecular and cell biologist at the University of Southern California, worries that more than 70 percent of Americans will die prematurely from diseases caused by or compounded by deficiencies of antioxidants. But starting young – in your 20s, 30s or 40s – can help keep your body youthful and disease-free instead of in need of repair later.

In fact, Packer insists that antioxidants "can make your heart strong, your mind

sharp and your body youthful well into your 70s, 80s, 90s and beyond. They can help prevent cancer, keep your skin supple and wrinkle-free, improve your sex life and extend your life."

Below is a list of 21 scientific studies showing why you need more than low doses of antioxidants, vitamins and minerals to soften the threat of premature aging and chronic diseases.

How High-Potency Supplements Can Save You

1. Vitamins E and C Prolong Life

Taking vitamin E and vitamin C (in higher doses than in a multivitamin) cut chances of death from all causes by 42 percent. Vitamin E users were 47 percent less apt to die of heart disease and 59 percent less likely to die of cancer, said the National Institute on Aging.

2. Vitamin E Boosts Immune System

Taking 200 IU of natural vitamin E daily boosted immune functioning in older people in Tufts University research. A supplement with only 60 milligrams of vitamin E daily did not improve immune functioning. Obviously, superior immune functioning lessens infections, and possibly cancer and heart disease.

3. Antioxidants Cut Death Rates

Men who took a special antioxidant capsule for seven years had 31 percent less cancer and 37 percent lower death rates than men getting a dummy pill or placebo, according to a French double-blind controlled study of 13,000 men and women aged 35 to 60. Doses in the daily capsule: 6 milligrams beta carotene, 120 milligrams vitamin C, 90 milligrams vitamin E, 100 micrograms selenium and 20 milligrams zinc.

4. Selenium Boosts Immunity and Mood

In a double-blind study of elderly people, researchers at the University of Brussels found taking 100 micrograms of selenium a day improved certain factors in immune functioning by 79 percent. One reason: The body needs selenium to produce a critical antioxidant enzyme that helps detoxify cellular fats that otherwise lower immunity, foster cancer and destroy arteries. A daily 100 micrograms of selenium also improved mood in a British study.

5. Vitamin C Prevents Heart Attacks

A Harvard study of 90,000 female nurses found that those who took 350-400 milligrams of vitamin C supplements daily for 16 years were 30 percent less apt to have a heart attack or other "coronary event" than non-vitamin C takers! Getting smaller amounts of vitamin C in foods did not prevent heart disease in the study. This surprising new evidence that vitamin C in supplements gave the heart stronger protection than vitamin C in food provides "compelling evidence" for taking vitamin C, say experts.

6. Vitamin E Stops Heart Attacks

A daily dose of 400 to 800 IU of natural vitamin E cut subsequent heart attacks in men with heart problems by an astonishing 77 percent in British research at Cambridge University. Other research shows it takes 400 IU of vitamin E to squelch toxicity (oxidation) of LDL cholesterol.

7. Vitamin C Drops Blood Pressure

Taking 500 mg of vitamin C daily reduced blood pressure in type-2 diabetics, finds an Irish study. After only a month, systolic pressure (the upper number) dropped ten points – down from 142 to 132 – and diastolic pressure fell about five points. Further, the vitamin C reduced the stiffness of arteries and the aorta, making them more flexible and able to dilate and contract properly.

8. B Vitamins Stop Strokes

High doses of B vitamins decreased the amount of plaque in carotid (neck) arteries by ten percent during a four-year study at the University of Toronto. Blocked carotid arteries can cause strokes. Plaque increased by 50 percent in non-vitamin B takers. Daily doses that reversed plaque: 250 micrograms B12, 25 milligrams B6 and 2500 micrograms folic acid. Researchers used the extra high dose of folic acid, but said it may not be necessary. They said 800 micrograms of folic acid is effective for most people.

9. Selenium Blocks Cancer

In a groundbreaking study of 1,312 older people, taking 200 micrograms of selenium daily for seven years slashed overall cancer rates by 42 percent and cancer death rates in half, compared with those taking a dummy (placebo) pill, according to University of Arizona research. Specifically, taking selenium cut the occurrence of prostate cancer by 69 percent; colorectal cancer, 64 percent; and lung cancer, 39 percent.

10. Vitamins Reduce Risk of Ovarian Cancer

Taking vitamin C reduced risk of the most common form of ovarian cancer by 60 percent. Taking vitamin E reduced risk 67 percent. Taking the two antioxidants together was most powerful, decreasing risk by 71 percent, according to a University of North Carolina study. Vitamin E and C in food alone did not deter the cancer. Daily protective dose (from food and pills) was more than 363 milligrams of vitamin C and more than 75 milligrams of vitamin E daily.

11. Lycopene Shrinks Prostate Tumors

Eating tomatoes, rich in the antioxidant lycopene, helps prevent prostate cancer, according to several studies. But taking lycopene supplements can shrink prostate tumors, according to Wayne State University investigators. They found that giving lycopene supplements to patients for only three weeks prior to surgery reduced prostate tumor size in 80 percent of men. More remarkable, the tumor did not spread beyond the prostate gland in 73 percent of men on lycopene; it did spread in 82 percent not getting lycopene.

12. Vitamin E Stops Bladder Cancer

You're less likely to die of bladder cancer if you take vitamin E long term says a new study by the American Cancer Society. Taking vitamin E supplements regularly (more than 15 times a month) for more than ten years reduced the risk of death from bladder cancer by 40 percent. Taking the vitamin for a shorter time did not affect bladder cancer mortality.

13. Vitamin C Builds Bones

Supplements of vitamin C stimulate the formation of collagen and bone, suggests research at the University of California, San Diego. Postmenopausal women who popped vitamin C pills for a dozen years or more had three percent higher bone mineral density (BMD) at several sites, indicating stronger bones, than nonusers. Women with the highest bone mineral density took 1000 milligrams or more of vitamin C a day.

14. Calcium and Vitamin D Prevent Fractures

Taking 500 milligrams of calcium and 700 IU of vitamin D daily for three years significantly cut the rate of bone loss and nonvertebral fractures in men and women older than age 65, reported Tufts University researchers.

15. Zinc Fends Off Rheumatoid Arthritis

A Mayo Clinic study found that older women who took various supplements were less apt to develop rheumatoid arthritis. Specifically, taking vitamin C or vitamin E cut risk by 30 percent. Taking zinc slashed risk over 60 percent. Eating lots of fruits and cruciferous vegetables (cabbage, cauliflower, Brussels sprouts and broccoli) also lowered risk of rheumatoid arthritis about 35 percent.

16. Vitamins Slow Mental Decline

Elderly women (ages 70 to 79) who were long-term, current users of vitamin E and vitamin C scored better on cognitive tests than women who had never used vitamins E or C. In the large Harvard study, vitamin takers were better able to recall words and the contents of a short paragraph, had better verbal fluency and ability on a numbers-backwards test. Women who had taken the vitamins the longest tended to have the highest scores.

17. Vitamin B12 Protects Brain

A recent US Department of Agriculture study showed that 40 percent of Americans, ages 26 to 83, had "low normal" B12 blood levels, sufficient to trigger neurological symptoms. Typical is low cognitive performance in children and high rates of depression, dementia and Alzheimer's disease in adults. Least deficient were those who took B12 supplements, or ate the most dairy foods and fortified cereals.

If you're over 50, you should take a B12 supplement, say experts. The low doses in "multis" help, but many older people need 500 or more micrograms daily. Three-thousand micrograms a day is considered a safe dose at which no adverse effects have been reported.

18. Vitamins Prevent Alzheimer's

Not a single older person who took separate doses of vitamin E (200 to 800 IU) or vitamin C (500 to1000 milligrams) developed Alzheimer's disease during a four-year double blind study at Chicago's Rush Institute for Healthy Aging. Subjects who took multivitamin supplements with low doses of vitamin E (typically 30 IU) or vitamin C (60 milligrams) were not protected from Alzheimer's.

19. Lutein Saves Vision

Taking ten milligrams a day of the antioxidant lutein actually reversed vision loss in patients with age-related macular degeneration, finds research at the Medical Center Eye Clinic and the University of Illinois in Chicago. After a year, the density of the macular pigment increased 50 percent in the lutein takers. More remarkable, they improved in visual acuity, contrast sensitivity and glare recovery. Adding other antioxidants to lutein improved vision even more.

20. Vitamin C Prevents Cataracts and Loss of Vision

Women taking vitamin C supplements cut their risk of cataracts by 77 per cent. In patients with early macular degeneration, taking daily doses of 500 milligrams of vitamin C, 400 IU vitamin E, 80 milligrams of zinc, 2 milligrams of copper and 15 milligrams of beta carotene for 11 years slowed progression to the advanced stage of loss of vision, according to a major study by the National Institutes of Health.

21. Vitamin C reduces inflammation.

Taking vitamin C (a daily dose of 515 milligrams) reduced blood levels of C-reactive protein (CRP), a marker of inflammation, by 24 percent, compared to taking a placebo in a clinical trial of 160 subjects at the University of California, Berkeley. This is important, because chronic inflammation is now believed to be a major contributor to artery clogging and heart attacks, strokes, diabetes and Alzheimer's disease. Using vitamin C to curb inflammation may help prevent such diseases, said researchers.

Vitamin C
Facts and Fiction

Confused about vitamin C? It's understandable. Much information about vitamin C is incomplete, misleading or wrong. Here leading authority Balz Frei, Ph.D., director of the Linus Pauling Institute at Oregon State University, answers the most common questions about vitamin C.

What is the most exciting new benefit of vitamin C?

Surprisingly, it's fighting heart disease. Vitamin C combats inflammation in blood vessels and helps stabilize plaque so it doesn't break off and create blockages. It also relaxes blood vessels, helping prevent high blood pressure, angina (chest pain) and mini-strokes. Several studies suggest that a high level of vitamin C in the blood lowers odds of heart disease by 25 to 60 percent. A likely effective dose: 200 to 500 milligrams of vitamin C daily. Taking 350 to 400 milligrams daily in a Harvard study of women slashed heart attack risk by one-third!

Can vitamin C prevent or cure cancer?

Vitamin-C packed fruits and vegetables appear to prevent cancer, but whether vitamin C is responsible is unclear, says Frei. Using large oral doses of vitamin C to treat cancer failed in a large Mayo Clinic Study. However, infusions of extremely high concentrations of vitamin C, as the late Linus Pauling advocated, may be toxic to cancer cells, Frei speculates. New tests are being considered to find out. Some doctors discourage taking vitamin C during chemotherapy, but Frei considers the antioxidant – at least in daily doses up to 500 – more beneficial than harmful to cancer patients.

Does taking vitamin C cure colds?

Popping high doses of vitamin C – 1000 milligrams or more – after you notice symptoms may cut the severity of a cold and its duration by a couple of days. But there's no evidence regular megadoses of vitamin C actually prevent colds. Still Frei says, "I tell people, if it works for them, go ahead."

Is Ester C (TM) a superior form of vitamin C?

"No. It's the most common question I get," says Frei. Contrary to advertising, your body doesn't know the difference between costly Ester C and plain old inexpensive ascorbic acid, a common form of vitamin C. "It's a marketing gimmick," says Frei.

How much vitamin C can your body use?

In recent National Institute of Health studies, cells become "saturated" with vitamin C at daily doses of 200 milligrams to 400 milligrams, indicating that's the maximum humans can absorb. But the research was conducted on healthy adults ages 25 to 30, so that's probably not an optimal dose for older people or those with infections, chronic inflammatory diseases or cancer, Frei concludes. A safer daily dose to cover the uncertainties of aging is 500 to 1000 milligrams, he says.

How safe is vitamin C?

"It's impossible to overdose on vitamin C," says Frei. Excesses are simply excreted, although high doses can cause diarrhea. Also, occasional accusations that vitamin C supplements promote kidney stones, clogged neck arteries or chromosome damage leading to cancer don't hold up. Since the body doesn't distinguish between vitamin C from pills and food, eating fruits and vegetables would cause the same harm, which is nonsensical.

Miraculous Magnesium

Chances are, you don't get enough magnesium. Americans' intake of magnesium dropped 50 percent in the last century. And the hidden health consequences are so alarming that most people would benefit from magnesium supplements, say experts.

A magnesium deficit underlies our epidemic of heart disease, high blood pressure, diabetes and osteoporosis, declares Lawrence Resnick, M.D. professor of medicine at Cornell Medical Center. Lacking magnesium, hearts beat irregularly, arteries stiffen, constrict and clog, blood pressure rises, blood tends to clot, muscles go into spasms, insulin grows weaker, blood sugar jumps, bones lose strength, pain signals intensify.

"Many people needlessly suffer pain – including fibromyalgia, migraines and muscle cramps – because they don't get enough magnesium," says Mildred Seelig, M.D., a leading magnesium researcher and adjunct professor, University of North Carolina.

Moreover, many people worsen the problem by loading up on calcium in efforts to combat osteoporosis. High calcium flushes magnesium from cells, creating electrical intracellular imbalances, a clear sign of many vascular diseases, says Dr.

HOW MUCH?

Most Americans probably need to take 150 to 250 milligrams of magnesium daily, says Dr. Seelig. Some need more. Seelig takes 400 milligrams a day. Although magnesium is of low toxicity, it may cause diarrhea in some who can't tolerate high doses. Cut back or build the dose up gradually; your body usually adapts, advises Seelig. Warning: Don't take magnesium if you have kidney disease, without consulting with your doctor.

Resnick. To avoid this, he urges getting at least one milligram of magnesium for each two milligrams of calcium.

Ten Important Ways Magnesium Helps:

1. Heart Arrhythmias: "People need to know that magnesium deficiency predisposes them to serious, even deadly, heart arrhythmias" – skipped, irregular and abnormally fast heart beats or atrial fibrillation – says cardiac specialist Michael Brodsky, M.D. at the College of Medicine of the Unversity of California, Irvine. In a British study, taking magnesium daily for six weeks reduced arrhythmias by 25 percent to 50 percent. In U.S. Department of Agriculture tests, women skimping on magnesium developed irregular heartbeats within three months. Magnesium supplements corrected the abnormality.

2. Blocked Arteries: High blood magnesium cuts your odds of dying from common "ischemic" heart disease (blocked or narrowed arteries) by one-third, say researchers at the Centers for Disease Control and Prevention. Other research shows that magnesium shortages lower good HDL cholesterol and accelerate atherosclerosis or "hardening of the arteries."

3. Blood Pressure: Cornell's Lawrence Resnick recently documented that the higher your magnesium inside your cells (intracellular) the more apt you are to have lower blood pressure, more elastic blood vessels and a less enlarged heart. He calls magnesium a natural calcium-channel blocker (blood-pressure drug), and says supplements can help normalize blood pressure.

4. Diabetes: "Diabetes is a magnesium deficiency state," says Jerry Nadler, M.D., of the University of Virginia School of Medicine. He finds that 80 percent of diabetics have low intracellular magnesium. Indeed, research suggests low magnesium boosts your risk of developing type 2 diabetes by one-third. Nadler says magnesium supplements can improve insulin activity, and may cut the risk and complications of diabetes. Some specialists tell diabetics to take 400 milligrams magnesium daily.

5. Strong Bones: Magnesium is as vital as calcium in building strong bones and preventing osteoporosis, says University of North Carolina's Mildred Seelig. "It's essential for normal bone metabolism." In a Swedish study, magnesium, but not calcium helped prevent hip fractures in older women. Tufts researchers found that high magnesium intake predicted higher bone mass and less bone loss in older people.

6. Migraines: Half of migraine sufferers have low magnesium, and upping magnesium has reduced the duration, intensity and frequency of migraines. Headache frequency dropped 42 percent in German adults who took 600 milligrams of magnesium daily for a month. Italian children given 122 milligrams to 366 milligrams magnesium daily had two-thirds fewer migraines after a month. Magnesium is now standard treatment at some headache clinics. One theory is that magnesium diminishes the brain blood vessel spasms involved in migraines.

7. Sound Sleep: Several studies show that a lack of magnesium can alter electrical activity in the brain, causing agitated sleep and frequent awakenings. "It looks like magnesium is important for a good night's sleep," says Forrest H. Nielsen, U.S. Department of Agriculture brain researcher.

8. Safer Pregnancy: Extensive research shows that magnesium lessens pre-eclampsia, in which blood pressure soars during late pregnancy, upping the risk of spontaneous abortions and premature, low birth-weight babies. A large British study of 10,000 women in 33 countries confirms that taking magnesium sulphate supplements reduced the hazard by 50 percent.

9. Pain Relief: If you have leg cramps or other muscle cramps, taking 100 milligrams to 400 milligrams of magnesium daily may bring relief, Seelig says. Extra magnesium may also help prevent or relieve painful myalgias, including the syndrome known as fibromyalgia, chronic lower back pain, restless-legs syndrome, erythromelagia (a painful dilation of skin blood vessels) and chronic fatigue syndrome. Seelig says magnesium reduces a pain-transmitter in the nervous system called substance P.

10. Extra Benefits: Taking magnesium could help treat premature ejaculation, prevent death from a congenital condition called long QT syndrome, treat Tourette's syndrome, relieve certain PMS symptoms (premenstrual syndrome), and prevent permanent hearing loss due to loud noises and damage to the auditory nerve.

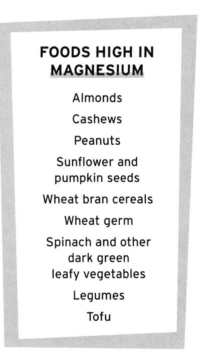

FOODS HIGH IN MAGNESIUM

Almonds

Cashews

Peanuts

Sunflower and pumpkin seeds

Wheat bran cereals

Wheat germ

Spinach and other dark green leafy vegetables

Legumes

Tofu

What Does
Jean Carper Take?

That is one of the most common questions I get from readers of my EatSmart column. Since I write regularly about research on vitamins, minerals and antioxidants, readers want to know what supplements I personally take and recommend to family and friends. It's a fair question.

After publication of my best-selling book *Stop Aging Now!* in 1995, I could find no single supplement on the market that fit the research in my book. Readers and myself were left on our own to assemble nearly 30 different vitamins, minerals and antioxidants that, in my opinion, research dictated could help combat chronic disease and premature aging. I felt obligated, as readers urged me to do, to develop a comprehensive multi-nutrient supplement to conform to the most up-to-date research.

The idea was to put the nutrients and antioxidants all together in one bottle to avoid shopping for and taking so many separate pills of unknown potency and quality. I produced the first *Stop Aging Now!*® Multi-Nutrient Formula in 1996. Since then I have exercised my unusual flexibility to quickly revise the formula to fit current research (I have no boards or marketers to consult) by adding or reducing a particular ingredient if I decide it's beneficial. Further, I determine the ingredient suppliers and how the supplements are made and tested. It is a source of comfort

to me, knowing that the multi-vitamin, mineral, antioxidant supplement I take, and recommend, is high quality, and widely accessible, costing less than a dollar a day.

In keeping with new research, and my recent book, Your Miracle Brain, I also take a *Stop Aging Now!*® Brain Energizer, that was formulated in consultation with experts, including Jerry Cott, Ph.D., a psychopharmacologist and former chief of the Pharmacologic Treatment Research Program at the National Institute of Mental Health. Also, I take glucosamine-chondroitin (*Stop Aging Now!*® Osteo-GC) believed to help combat the pain and progression of osteoarthritis. And, as extra insurance, I take a *Stop Aging Now!*® High-Antioxidant Green Tea Extract capsule.

How to Get More Info on *Stop Aging Now!*® Supplements

To get more information or to order the *Stop Aging Now!*® supplements that I take, you can call 800-627-9721 or visit my websites jeancarper.com or stopagingnow.com.

PART 3

The Recipes

Black Bean Salsa

1½   **pounds tomatoes, diced**

1   **15-ounce can black beans,
     drained and rinsed, or homecooked**

1   **cup cooked yellow corn kernels**

1   **medium jalapeño pepper, seeded and finely minced**

½   **cup chopped red onion**

2   **cloves garlic, chopped or crushed**

1   **cup minced fresh cilantro**

1   **tablespoon canola oil**

2   **tablespoons fresh lime juice**

1   **teaspoon honey**

    Hot sauce, cayenne pepper and salt, to taste

Combine all. Refrigerate 2 hours to let the flavors combine. Serve with baked tortilla chips or low-fat crackers.

Makes about 4 cups.

Per ½ cup: 94 calories, 2.5g total fat, (0.3g saturated), 16g carbohydrate, 3.6g protein, 3.8g fiber, 99mg sodium.

WHY IT'S GOOD FOR YOU:

* High antioxidants in tomatoes, corn, onion, garlic and cilantro

* High fiber and high protein in beans

* Hot peppers are good for lungs

* Plus: Beans are low glycemic index and suppress blood sugar

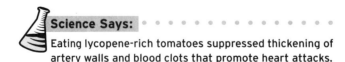

Science Says: • • • • • • • • • • • • •
Eating lycopene-rich tomatoes suppressed thickening of artery walls and blood clots that promote heart attacks.

• • • • • • • • • • • • • • •

Quick Guacamole

1 **medium, ripe Hass avocado, mashed**
1 **teaspoon fresh lemon or lime juice**
1 **large garlic clove, crushed**
   Hot sauce, such as Tabasco, to taste
   Salt and freshly ground black pepper, to taste

Mix all the ingredients.
Serve with baked tortilla chips.

Serves 2.

Per serving: 166 calories, 15.4g fat (2.5g saturated),
8g carbohydrate, 2.1g protein, 2g fiber, 16mg sodium.

**WHY IT'S GOOD
FOR YOU:**
*High potassium, anti-
  oxidants and good fat
  in avocado
*Hot sauce clears lungs

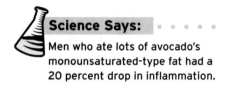

Science Says: . . . . .
Men who ate lots of avocado's
monounsaturated-type fat had a
20 percent drop in inflammation.

Zesty Mexican Bean Dip

2   **15-ounce cans pinto beans, preferably no-salt-added,* 1 can drained and rinsed**

1½   **teaspoons ground cumin or to taste**

1   **teaspoon chili powder or to taste**

2   **tablespoons fresh lemon juice**

Hot sauce, such as Tabasco, or jalapeño peppers, to taste

Salt, to taste

Place the beans and seasonings in a food processor or blender. Process until smooth and creamy. Serve with fresh vegetables, tortillas or crackers.

Makes about 3 cups.

Serves 12.

Per ¼-cup serving: 41 calories, 0.4g total fat, 7g carbohydrate, 2.7g protein, 2g fiber, 117mg sodium. *With no-salt added beans, the sodium drops to 11mg per serving.

WHY IT'S GOOD FOR YOU:

* High fiber, protein in beans

* Lemon juice suppresses blood sugar rises

* **Plus:** Beans beat most fruits and vegetables in anti-oxidant activity

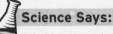

Science Says: • • • • • • • •

Dried beans pack more protein than any other plant food, plus fiber, B vitamins, zinc, potassium, magnesium, calcium and iron.

• • • • • • • • • • • • • • • • •

Gorgonzola-Tofu Dip with Walnuts

8 ounces soft tofu, mashed

3 tablespoons soft or crumbled Gorgonzola

3 tablespoons chopped walnuts

¼ cup finely chopped onions

¼ cup fat-free sour cream

Salt, to taste

Combine all. Serve with apple wedges
or sesame flatbread.

Makes 1½ cups.

Per tablespoon: 16 calories, 1g total fat (0.2g saturated),
1g carbohydrate, 1g protein, 0g fiber, 14mg sodium.

**WHY IT'S GOOD
FOR YOU:**

＊High antioxidants
in tofu and onions

＊Good fat in walnuts

＊**Plus:** Tofu may lower
risk of heart disease,
osteoporosis and
prostate cancer

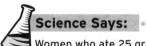 **Science Says:**

Women who ate 25 grams of soy protein a day, such
as tofu and soy milk, for six weeks showed improved
functioning of arteries and less inflammation.

Chicken Saté with Easy Peanut Sauce

1 **pound boneless, skinless chicken breast, cut into 6-inch x 1-inch strips**

Olive or canola oil

Thread chicken on 12 small skewers. Brush or spray with olive or canola oil. Grill or broil until done, about 7 minutes, turning once.

Serve with Easy Peanut Dipping Sauce.

Makes 12 appetizers.

Per serving: 173 calories, 10g total fat (1.6g saturated), 3g carbohydrate, 8.6g protein, 1g fiber, 248mg sodium.

Easy Peanut Dipping Sauce

½ **cup smooth peanut butter, preferably natural**

¼ **teaspoon red pepper flakes**

1 **tablespoon reduced-sodium soy sauce**

1 **garlic clove, crushed**

1 **teaspoon curry powder**

¾ **cup fat-free, reduced-sodium chicken broth**

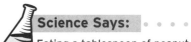

Science Says:

Eating a tablespoon of peanut butter (or nuts) five times a week reduced women's odds of diabetes by 20 percent in Harvard research.

Combine all in a microwave-safe bowl. Microwave, covered, on high 2 minutes or until smooth. If too thick, add more broth.

Makes about 1¼ cups.

Per 1 tablespoon: 40 calories, 3g total fat (0.7 g saturated), 1.4g carbohydrate, 1.8g protein, 0.4g fiber, 82mg sodium.

Fresh Spring Rolls with Thai Dipping Sauce

6   spring roll wrappers, available in Asian markets

12 medium shrimp, cooked and peeled

1   cup shredded garden lettuce

1/3 cup chopped fresh cilantro

1/2 cup peeled, seeded, chopped cucumber

1   medium carrot, julienned

WHY IT'S GOOD FOR YOU:
* Antioxidants in lettuce, cilantro, cucumber and carrots
* Low fat, high protein in shrimp

In a bowl of cool water, soak a wrapper until it is limp. Lay wrapper out flat. Place 1/6 of each ingredient down middle of wrapper with lettuce first. Fold over each end, then roll wrapper around contents, as if making a burrito. Moisten at seam and press to close. Slice in two. Repeat with the remaining wrappers and filling ingredients. Serve with Quick Thai dipping sauce.

Makes 6 appetizer-size rolls.

Per serving: 49 calories, 4g total fat (0.1g saturated), 7g carbohydrate, 4g protein, 0.7g fiber, 75mg sodium.

Quick Thai Dipping Sauce

1   tablespoon reduced-sodium soy sauce

1   tablespoon white wine or rice vinegar

3   tablespoons mirin (sweetened rice wine)

1/4 teaspoon grated fresh ginger, optional

Science Says:
Shrimp is a good low-fat, high-protein alternative to meat and does not raise cholesterol.

Combine all ingredients in a small bowl.

Makes about 1/3 cup.

Per tablespoon: 27 calories, 0g total fat, 4g carbohydrate, 0.2g protein, 0g fiber, 120 mg sodium.

Nutty Broccoli Appetizers

- ¼ cup finely chopped onions
- 4 cloves garlic, crushed
- 1 tablespoon extra-virgin olive oil
- 1 10-ounce package frozen chopped broccoli
- 1 cup bread crumbs, preferably whole-wheat
- ¼ cup chopped walnuts
- ¼ cup freshly grated Parmesan cheese
- ½ teaspoon each dried oregano and basil
- 2 eggs or ½ cup egg substitute, slightly whipped
    Salt and freshly ground black pepper, to taste

WHY IT'S GOOD FOR YOU:
- *High antioxidants in broccoli, garlic and onions
- *Magnesium and other nutrients in walnuts
- *Good fat in olive oil
- *Plus: Anti-cancer activity in broccoli

Preheat oven to 400°F

Sauté onions and garlic in olive oil. Cook broccoli according to package directions; squeeze out excess water. Cool slightly. Combine with remaining ingredients. Form into balls 1½ inches in diameter. Place on nonstick baking sheet. Spray balls with olive oil or canola spray. Bake in oven 20-30 minutes, or until brown. Serve warm or at room temperature.

Makes 24 balls.

Note: You also can spread mixture in a shallow pan, bake and cut into squares.

Per ball: 33 calories, 1.9g total fat (0.4g saturated), 3g carbohydrate, 1.9g protein, 0.5g fiber, 41mg sodium.

As a dip for the balls, you can use Quick Thai Dipping Sauce or Easy Peanut Dipping Sauce, pages 62-63.

Science Says: • • • • • • • • • • • • • • •
Five to six daily servings of vegetables cut stroke-risk by one-third. Most potent are leafy greens, such as broccoli and spinach.
• • • • • • • • • • • • • • • • • •

Light Salmon Mousse

1   14¾ ounce can red or pink salmon, drained (reserve liquid)

1   cup plain fat-free yogurt

1   cup fat-free cottage cheese

1   packet unflavored gelatin

¼   cup chopped fresh dill

    Freshly ground black pepper, to taste

1   cup thinly sliced, peeled cucumber

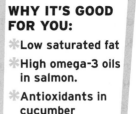

WHY IT'S GOOD FOR YOU:
* Low saturated fat
* High omega-3 oils in salmon.
* Antioxidants in cucumber

Place salmon in large bowl. Remove skin. Mash fish, including bones. In a blender or with a mixer, combine yogurt and cottage cheese. Add salmon and chopped dill. In a small saucepan, soften gelatin in reserved salmon liquid. Stir over low heat until dissolved, about 2 minutes. Add to salmon; mix thoroughly.

Line bottom of 3- to 4-cup mold, bowl or loaf cake pan with cucumber slices. Pour in salmon mixture. Chill 2-3 hours until set. Unmold and serve with crackers or bread.

Serves 10-12 as appetizer.

Per serving: 77 calories, 12.3g total fat (0.5g saturated), 3g carbohydrate, 0.6g protein, 0.2g fiber, 264mg sodium

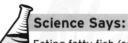

Science Says: •
Eating fatty fish (salmon, tuna, sardines or herring) twice a week cut endometrial cancer risk 40 percent in women. Lean fish did not.

Oysters Rockefeller

1   tablespoon extra-virgin olive oil

2   cloves garlic, crushed

1   10-ounce package frozen chopped spinach,
    thawed and squeezed very dry

¼   cup fat-free cream cheese

¼   cup fat-free half and half
    Salt and freshly ground pepper to taste
    Dash of ground nutmeg

1   pint shelled oysters, drained,
    rinsed and patted dry

¼   cup grated Parmesan cheese
    hot pepper sauce, to taste

WHY IT'S GOOD FOR YOU:

* Super antioxidants in spinach
* Plus: Oysters are rich in immune-boosting, anti-cancer zinc

Preheat oven to 400°F. In a small skillet, sauté garlic in oil until soft; add spinach, cream cheese and half and half. Sauté, stirring, until blended, about 5 minutes. Stir in salt, pepper and nutmeg. Spread spinach mixture over bottom of 10-inch pie plate or ovenproof dish. Top with oysters; sprinkle on cheese and hot sauce. Bake for 15 minutes. If needed, briefly broil to brown.

Serves 6.

Per serving: 168 calories, 8g total fat (2g saturated), 11g carbohydrate, 13g protein, 2g fiber, 336mg sodium.

Science Says: • • • • • • • • • • • •

Women who ate foods highest in zinc, such as oysters, were one-third as likely to have breast cancer as women who ate foods lowest in zinc, finds a German study.

• • • • • • • • • • • • • • • • • • •

Pasta Appetizer with Brazil-Nut Sauce

- 4 ounces spaghetti
- 2 large cloves garlic, crushed or minced
- 3 tablespoons extra-virgin olive oil or macadamia nut oil
- ½ cup chopped fresh parsley
- ½ cup sliced black olives
- 2 tablespoons capers (optional)
- 2½ ounces Brazil nuts, coarsely ground in a blender

Salt and freshly ground pepper, to taste

WHY IT'S GOOD FOR YOU:

- * Anti-cancer selenium in Brazil nuts
- * Antioxidants in garlic, parsley and olives
- * Good mono-unsaturated fat in olive oil

Cook spaghetti until al dente. While pasta is cooking, sauté garlic in oil over medium heat. Add oil and garlic to drained pasta. Stir in parsley, olives, capers, half the ground nuts, salt and pepper. Transfer to plates and top with remaining nuts.

Note: The ground nuts have the appearance and texture of grated Parmesan cheese.

Serves 4 as an appetizer.

Per serving: 336 calories, 24g total fat (4.5g saturated, 13g monounsaturated), 26g carbohydrate, 4g fiber, 7g protein, 152mg sodium.

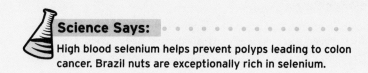

Science Says: High blood selenium helps prevent polyps leading to colon cancer. Brazil nuts are exceptionally rich in selenium.

Spicy Mixed Nuts

1   **egg white**

2   **tablespoons cold water**

2/3   **cup each walnuts, pecans and almonds**

1/2   **cup sugar**

1½   **teaspoons cinnamon**

1/4   **teaspoon each ground ginger and nutmeg**

Beat egg white and water until frothy. Stir nuts into mixture to coat, then drain slightly in a colander, 3-4 minutes. Mix sugar and spices in a plastic bag. Add nuts and shake to coat. Spread wet nut mixture in a single layer on a microwave-safe plate; microwave on high for 1½ minutes, or until mixture is bubbly. Stir. Microwave another 1½ minutes. Remove from oven and stir to separate. Cool. Store in a sealed container.

Makes 2 cups.

Per 1/4-cup serving: 235 calories, 17g total fat (1.6 saturated, 9 monounsaturated), 18g carbohydrate, 5g protein, 2g fiber, 9mg sodium.

Science Says:
Adding cinnamon to foods helps suppress blood sugar by boosting insulin activity and cells' ability to process glucose.

Terrific Trail Mix

1   cup combination diced dried fruit, such as prunes, apricots, pears and apples

½   cup raisins and/or dried cherries or cranberries

1½ cups unsalted sunflower seeds

1   cup unsalted dry-roasted peanuts or honey-roasted peanuts, chopped walnuts or unsalted almonds

Mix all.

Makes 4 cups.

Per ¼-cup serving: 165 calories, 11.3g total fat (1.3g saturated), 14g carbohydrate, 5.6g protein, 1.4g fiber, 2mg sodium.

WHY IT'S GOOD FOR YOU:
* Extremely high antioxidants in dried fruit
* Magnesium in sunflower seeds
* Peanuts are low glycemic, curb blood sugar

Science Says:
Raisins are high in antioxidants and produce beneficial changes in the colon that may help protect against colon cancer.

Curried Lentil Soup

1	tablespoon canola oil
1	cup chopped onion
2	cloves garlic, crushed
2	tablespoons curry powder
4	cups fat-free, reduced-sodium chicken broth
2½	cups water
2	cups chopped canned tomatoes, with liquid
2	cups raw lentils
1	cup finely chopped carrots
½	cup red wine, optional
1	cup chopped fresh parsley
	Salt and freshly ground black pepper, to taste

WHY IT'S GOOD FOR YOU:

* Lentils suppress blood sugar

* Antioxidants in garlic, onion, tomatoes, carrots and parsley

* Plus: Curcumin in curry is an anti-inflammatory

Heat oil in a large saucepan over medium heat. Sauté onion and garlic until soft. Stir in curry powder; sauté 1 minute. Add broth, water, tomatoes, lentils, carrots and optional wine. Simmer, covered, until lentils are cooked, about 30 minutes. Stir in parsley; simmer 5 minutes. Season with salt and pepper. Serve with sourdough bread.

Serves 8.

Per serving: 218 calories, 2.6g total fat (0.2g saturated), 35g carbohydrate, 16g protein, 7.6g fiber, 378mg sodium.

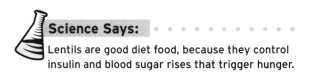

Science Says: Lentils are good diet food, because they control insulin and blood sugar rises that trigger hunger.

Corn Chowder with Shrimp

1 medium yellow onion, chopped

1 red or green bell pepper, seeded and diced

1 tablespoon extra-virgin olive oil

2½ cups fat-free milk

1½ cups evaporated fat-free milk (1 12-ounce can)

2 medium baking potatoes, peeled and diced

2 cups frozen or canned yellow corn kernels

1 pound large or medium shrimp, peeled and deveined

Salt and freshly ground black pepper, to taste

⅓ cup chopped fresh cilantro

In a large pot, sauté onion and pepper in olive oil until soft, about 12 minutes. Add milk, evaporated milk, potatoes and corn. Cover. Slowly bring to a boil and simmer over low heat until potatoes are tender, about 10 minutes. Add shrimp and cook about 3 minutes or until shrimp turns pink. Do not overcook shrimp. Add more skim milk if needed. Season with salt and pepper. Ladle into bowls and top with cilantro.

Serves 6.

Per serving: 278 calories, 4.2g total fat (0.8g saturated), 38g carbohydrate, 24g protein, 2.7g fiber, 224mg sodium.

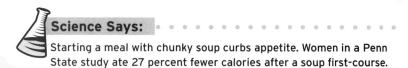

Science Says: Starting a meal with chunky soup curbs appetite. Women in a Penn State study ate 27 percent fewer calories after a soup first-course.

Ginger Carrot Soup

2   **large yellow onions, chopped (2 cups)**

1   **tablespoon extra-virgin olive oil**

1   **pound carrots, cut into chunks**

2   **cups fat-free, reduced-sodium chicken broth**

2   **tablespoons minced crystallized ginger or 2 teaspoons ground ginger**

1   **teaspoon ground cinnamon**

1½   **cups orange juice**

½   **cup fat-free half-and-half**

    Fresh chives, for garnish

In a large pot, sauté onions in olive oil until soft. Add carrots, broth, ginger and cinnamon; simmer until carrots are thoroughly cooked. Transfer mixture to a blender or food processor and process until smooth. Stir in orange juice and half-and-half. Serve warm or chilled, garnished with snipped chives.

Serves 4.

Per serving: 207 calories, 3.8g total fat (0.5g saturated), 33g carbohydrate, 4g protein, 5g fiber, 364mg sodium.

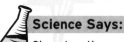

Science Says: •
Ginger's active component, gingerol, when fed to laboratory mice, blocked development and growth of tumors, in University of Minnesota research.
• • • • • • • • • • • • • • • • • • • •

Eye-Saving Bean Soup with Kale

1 tablespoon extra-virgin olive oil or canola oil

1 medium yellow onion, chopped

8 large cloves garlic, crushed or minced

4 cups chopped raw kale or 1 10-ounce package frozen chopped kale, thawed and squeezed to remove excess water

4 cups fat-free, reduced-sodium chicken or vegetable broth

4 plum tomatoes, chopped

2 15-ounce cans white beans, such as cannellini or navy, undrained, about 3 cups

2 teaspoons dried Italian herb seasoning or 1 teaspoon each dried thyme and rosemary

Salt and freshly ground pepper, to taste

1 cup chopped fresh parsley

WHY IT'S GOOD FOR YOU:

* A super dose of antioxidant lutein – 7 mg per serving

* High antioxidants in onions, tomatoes, garlic and herbs

* High fiber in beans

* Very low fat

* **Plus:** Beans discourage blood sugar rises, heart disease, diabetes and cancer

In a large pot, heat olive oil. Add onion and garlic and sauté until soft. Add kale and sauté, stirring until wilted. Add 3 cups of broth, 2 cups of beans, and all of the tomato, herbs, salt and pepper. Simmer 5 minutes.

In a blender or food processor, mix the remaining beans and broth until smooth. Stir into soup to thicken. Simmer 15 minutes. Ladle into bowls; sprinkle with chopped parsley.

Serves 8.

Per serving: 133 calories, 2.4g total fat (0.3g saturated), 23g carbohydrate, 10 g protein, 6g fiber, 283mg sodium.

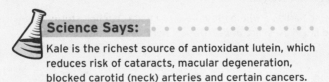

Science Says:

Kale is the richest source of antioxidant lutein, which reduces risk of cataracts, macular degeneration, blocked carotid (neck) arteries and certain cancers.

Old-fashioned Vegetable-Barley Soup

1   tablespoon extra-virgin olive oil

1   medium yellow onion, chopped

2   large cloves garlic, crushed or minced

3/4 cup sliced carrots

1   cup cauliflower, in thick slices or chunks

2   cups canned no-salt-added diced tomatoes

4   cups fat-free, reduced-sodium chicken
     or vegetable broth

1   cup pearl barley

1   cup fresh spinach leaves, torn into pieces

5   drops hot chili sauce, optional

     Salt and freshly ground black pepper, to taste

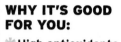

WHY IT'S GOOD FOR YOU:

* High antioxidants in vegetables
* High fiber in barley
* Low fat

In a large saucepan, heat oil. Add onions, garlic and carrots to the pan, stirring until onions begin to soften, about 3 minutes. Add cauliflower, tomatoes, barley, and broth. Simmer, partially covered, for 20-25 minutes. Stir in spinach and seasonings and simmer an additional 5 minutes.

Serves 6.

Per serving: 188 calories, 2.9g total fat (0.4g saturated), 35g carbohydrate, 7g protein, 7.4g fiber, 409mg sodium.

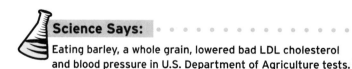

Science Says: Eating barley, a whole grain, lowered bad LDL cholesterol and blood pressure in U.S. Department of Agriculture tests.

Hearty Asian Mushroom Soup

4 cups fat-free, reduced-sodium chicken broth

2 tablespoons reduced-sodium soy sauce

2 teaspoons grated fresh ginger

3 cloves garlic, crushed

3 cups assorted sliced or diced mushrooms, such as white button, stemmed shiitake, portobello, crimini or oyster

1 cup thinly sliced carrots

3 cups white cabbage cut into small wedges

2 cups shredded or cubed cooked chicken breast

2 cups fresh or cooked udon noodles (substitute 2 cups cooked linguine)

1 cup thinly sliced scallions with some green tops

2 cups sliced raw spinach or whole baby spinach leaves

   Freshly ground black pepper, to taste

1 tablespoon mirin (sweetened rice wine), optional

WHY IT'S GOOD FOR YOU:

* Garlic and ginger are blood thinners
* Mushrooms fight infections and cancer
* Antioxidants in carrots, cabbage, scallions and spinach
* Very low fat

In a large pot, combine broth, soy sauce, ginger, garlic, mushrooms, carrots, cabbage and chicken. Cover, bring to a boil and simmer until mushrooms are soft, about 5 minutes. Stir in noodles, scallions and spinach; simmer until greens are wilted, about 2 minutes. Season with pepper. For a little sweetness, stir in optional mirin.

Serves 6

Per serving: 163 calories, 2.6g total fat (0.5g saturated), 16g carbohydate, 19g protein, 3g fiber, 860mg sodium.

Science Says:

Portobello, shiitake, crimini, button and large white mushrooms contain estrogen-reducing chemicals that may help ward off breast cancer.

Out-of-This-World Thai Crab Soup

1	14-ounce can lite coconut milk
½	cup creamy peanut butter, preferably natural
4	small ripe bananas, sliced
6	cups bottled clam juice or homemade fish stock
2	cups dry white wine
8	scallions, thinly sliced with green
3	tablespoons reduced-sodium soy sauce
2½	tablespoons hot chili paste or to taste
12	ounces fresh bean sprouts
1	pound backfin crabmeat*
1	cup chopped fresh cilantro
	Juice of 1 lime

WHY IT'S GOOD FOR YOU:

* Anti-cancer agents in scallions
* High vitamin B6 and potassium in bananas
* Very low fat
* High protein in crab

In a blender, puree coconut milk, peanut butter and bananas. Transfer to a large pot; add clam juice or fish stock, white wine, scallions, soy sauce and chili paste. Cover and simmer 5 minutes. Add bean sprouts, crabmeat, ½ cup of the cilantro and lime juice. Simmer 5 minutes covered. Add remaining ½ cup cilantro just before serving.

*You can substitute 2½ cups less expensive imitation crabmeat or other whitefish.

Serves 12 as an appetizer soup, 8 as a main dish.

Per serving as an appetizer: 204 calories, 8.8g total fat (2.3g saturated), 15g carbohydrate, 13g protein, 1.7g fiber, 595mg sodium.

Science Says: Eating crab helped lower blood cholesterol in University of Washington studies.

Curry-Squash-Apple Soup

1   12-ounce package frozen winter squash
2   cups fat-free, low-sodium chicken or vegetable broth
1½ cups unsweetened applesauce
2   teaspoons curry powder, or to taste
    Salt, to taste
    Fat-free sour cream, for garnish

In a microwave-safe dish, microwave squash on high power until mushy. Stir in broth, applesauce, curry powder and salt. Microwave 5 minutes or until hot. Process in a blender for 15 seconds. Serve topped with a dollop of sour cream.

Serves 4.

Per serving: 98 calories, 0.3g total fat (.01g saturated), 23 g carbohydrate, 3.2g protein, 5g fiber, 289g sodium.

WHY IT'S GOOD FOR YOU:
* High beta carotene in squash
* High antioxidants in apples
* Curry powder is anti-inflammatory and anti-cancer

Science Says: Apple antioxidants have aspirin-like anticoagulant activity.

Snappy Gazpacho

1   **small cucumber, peeled and sliced**

1   **medium bell pepper, preferably red, cored, seeded and cut into chunks**

1   **small zucchini, peeled and cut into chunks**

1   **medium onion, chopped**

2   **medium tomatoes, peeled and quartered**

2   **cloves garlic, minced or crushed**

3   **cups tomato juice, preferably low-sodium**

¼   **cup chopped fresh cilantro**

½   **teaspoon hot chili sauce, such as Tabasco**

2   **tablespoons distilled white vinegar or fresh lemon juice**

WHY IT'S GOOD FOR YOU:

＊Antioxidants in cucumber, peppers, zucchini, onion, tomatoes and cilantro

＊Very low calories and fat

Put all ingredients in a blender or food processor and combine until chunky. Chill and serve. If you like, garnish with croutons.

Serves 6.

Per serving: 56 calories, 0.4g total fat, 13g carbohydrate, 2.4g protein, 3g fiber, 448mg sodium.

Science Says: Eating raw onions raised good HDL cholesterol in three out of four heart patients in Tufts University research.

Grilled Vegetable Gazpacho

1   red bell pepper, halved, seeded and grilled

1   yellow bell pepper, halved, seeded and grilled

1   large red onion, halved or sliced and grilled

1   large red tomato, unpeeled

1   large yellow tomato, unpeeled

1   11.5-ounce can "spicy" V-8 juice

1   tablespoon chopped fresh basil

1   teaspoon balsamic vinegar

   Dash hot sauce

Chop all vegetables. Put half in blender with the V-8 juice and seasonings. Blend until smooth. Add remaining chopped vegetables. Chill and serve.

Serves 6.

Per serving: 49 calories, 0.3g total fat, 11g carbohydrate, 1.9g protein, 2.2g fiber, 176mg sodium.

Note: This is an excellent way to use leftover grilled vegetables

Science Says: • • • • • • • •

In a University of North Carolina study, drinking V-8 juice daily reduced lung cell DNA damage in those exposed to air pollution.

Creamy Broccoli Soup

1 10-ounce package frozen chopped broccoli
   or 2 cups fresh florets

2 cloves garlic, halved

1 medium onion, chopped

1 15-ounce can fat-free, reduced-sodium chicken broth

2 tablespoons fresh lemon juice

1 cup fat-free sour cream

½ cup fat-free milk

½ teaspoon ground nutmeg

   Salt and freshly ground black pepper, to taste

   Croutons, optional

   Freshly grated Parmesan, optional

Place broccoli, garlic, onion and 2 tablespoons chicken broth in a microwave-safe dish. Microwave, covered, on high until onions are soft (10-12 minutes), stopping once to break up the frozen broccoli. Put the vegetables, lemon juice and remaining broth in a blender; puree. Blend in sour cream, milk and seasonings. Chill. Serve topped with optional croutons or Parmesan cheese.

Serves 4.

Per serving: 105 calories, 0.9g total fat, 16g carbohydrate, 6.5g protein, 2g fiber, 364mg sodium.

Science Says:
Broccoli is packed with a unique antioxidant — sulforaphane glucosinolate — that boosts your body's ability to detoxify cancer-causing agents.

Cold Avocado Soup

1   medium, ripe Hass avocado, cut into chunks

1   tablespoon fresh lemon juice

1½   cups fat-free, reduced-sodium vegetable broth
     or chicken broth

¾   cup fat-free sour cream

1   teaspoon ground cumin

     Salt, to taste

     Dash of hot chili sauce, optional

     Chopped fresh cilantro or parsley, for garnish

     Tomato salsa or diced fresh tomatoes, for garnish

Combine avocado, lemon juice, broth, sour cream, cumin, salt and chili sauce in a blender: puree until smooth. Chill for 1 to 2 hours. Serve garnished with chopped fresh cilantro or parsley and salsa or diced tomatoes.

Serves 2.

Per serving: 287 calories, 15.6g total fat (2.5g saturated), 29g carbohydrate, 9.6g protein, 2.1g fiber, 274mg sodium.

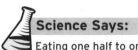

Science Says: • • • • •

Eating one half to one-and-a-half small avocados a day for three weeks reduced cholesterol eight percent in Australian studies.

Caribbean Black Bean Soup

4 cups cooked no-salt-added black beans
(3 15-ounce cans, drained and rinsed)

1½ cups fat-free plain yogurt, plus extra for garnish

1 4.5-ounce can mild peeled green chiles

2 teaspoons ground cumin

½ teaspoon balsamic vinegar or lemon juice

Salt and freshly ground black pepper, to taste

1 tablespoon snipped chives or sliced scallion greens

In a blender or food processor, puree beans, yogurt, chiles, cumin, vinegar or lemon juice, salt and pepper. Serve cold, topped with a dollop of yogurt and sprinkled with chives or scallions.

Serves 4.

Per serving: 292 calories, 1g total fat, 51g carbohydrate, 21g protein, 16g fiber, 337mg sodium.

WHY IT'S GOOD FOR YOU:

* Beans are high in folic acid and fiber
* Yogurt fights infections and is good for blood sugar
* Plus: Beans lower cholesterol, keep blood sugar stable and contain anti-cancer compounds

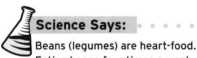

Science Says:

Beans (legumes) are heart-food. Eating beans four times a week, compared with once a week, cut heart disease risk 22 percent in a Tulane University study.

Tomato Bisque in a Blender

2   **14.5-ounce cans no-salt-added diced tomatoes or 4 cups peeled fresh tomatoes**

1   **cup fat-free plain yogurt**

¼   **teaspoon hot sauce, such as Tabasco**

2   **large cloves garlic, crushed**

1¼   **teaspoons prepared horseradish**

    Salt and freshly ground black pepper, to taste

1   **ripe Hass avocado, cubed, optional**

Put all ingredients but avocado in blender or food processor. Puree until smooth. Serve chilled or at room temperature, ladled over avocado cubes, if desired.

Serves 4.

Per serving: 77 calories, 0.6g total fat (0.1g saturated), 14g carbohydrate, 5g protein, 1.4g fiber, 84mg sodium.

WHY IT'S GOOD FOR YOU:

* High anti-cancer lycopene in tomatoes

* Horseradish and hot sauce help breathing

* Beneficial bacteria in yogurt

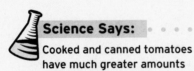

Science Says: · · · ·

Cooked and canned tomatoes have much greater amounts of bioavailable antioxidant lycopene than raw tomatoes.

· · · · · · · · · · · · ·

Spinach and Berries with Curry Dressing

6   ounces fresh spinach (about 6 cups),
    washed, dried and torn into bite-size pieces

1   cup thickly sliced strawberries

1   cup blueberries, any stems removed

1   small red onion, thinly sliced

½   cup chopped pecans

Fat-free Curry Dressing

2   tablespoons balsamic vinegar

2   tablespoons rice vinegar

1   tablespoon plus 1 teaspoon honey

1   teaspoon curry powder

2   teaspoons Dijon mustard

    Salt and freshly ground black pepper, to taste

WHY IT'S GOOD FOR YOU:

*Super-high antioxidants in spinach and berries

*Plus: Curry powder is anti-inflammatory

Whisk together dressing ingredients. Add to spinach and toss lightly. Add berries, onion and pecans. Toss lightly and serve.

Serves 6.

Per serving: 117 calories, 6.4 total g fat (0.5 g saturated,) 14g carbohydrate, 2g protein, 3g fiber, 67mg sodium.

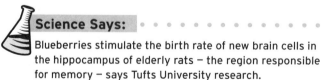

Science Says:

Blueberries stimulate the birth rate of new brain cells in the hippocampus of elderly rats – the region responsible for memory – says Tufts University research.

Spinach and Arugula with Radishes

6   cups mixed baby greens, including spinach, arugula and lettuces

1   cup very thinly sliced red radishes

⅓   cup shredded mint leaves

¼   cup pine nuts, toasted

Honey-Mustard Dressing

1   tablespoon extra-virgin olive oil

1   tablespoon honey

3   tablespoons rice vinegar

2   teaspoons Dijon mustard

  Salt and freshly ground black pepper, to taste

WHY IT'S GOOD FOR YOU:

* Super-high anti-oxidants in spinach and arugula
* Very low-calorie, low-fat, low-sodium
* Plus: Vinegar suppresses rises in blood sugar

In a large bowl, combine greens, radishes, mint and nuts.
Whisk together oil, honey, vinegar and mustard.
Add to salad and toss lightly. Grind on black pepper.

Serves 6.

Per serving: 88 calories, 5g fat (0.8g saturated), 9g carbohydrate, 3g protein, 3g fiber, 102mg sodium

Science Says: • • • • • • • • • • •
Women who eat the most spinach and other greens lower their odds of breaking a hip by 30 percent. Leafy greens are high in bone-protecting vitamin K.
• • • • • • • • • • • • • • •

Spinach with Orange and Ginger Dressing

4   cups baby spinach leaves, washed and dried

1   Hass avocado, diced

1   large orange, peeled, sliced and seeded

Dressing:

1   tablespoon extra-virgin olive oil

¼   cup orange juice concentrate

1   teaspoon fresh lemon juice

2   teaspoons grated fresh ginger

     Salt and freshly ground black pepper, to taste

WHY IT'S GOOD FOR YOU:

* High antioxidants in spinach and orange
* Good fat and antioxidants in avocado
* **Plus:** Ginger is anti-inflammatory

Divide the spinach among four salad plates. Top with avocado and orange. Whisk together dressing; drizzle on each salad. Top with freshly ground black pepper.

Serves 4.

Per serving: 170 calories, 11.5g total fat (1.7g saturated), 17g carbohydrate, 3g protein, 3.5g fiber, 50mg sodium.

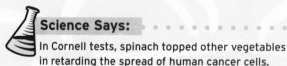

Science Says:

In Cornell tests, spinach topped other vegetables in retarding the spread of human cancer cells. Next in order: cabbage, red pepper, onion and broccoli.

Spinach with Pears and Blue Cheese

3   cups baby spinach, washed and dried

3   medium, ripe yellow pears, cored but not peeled, and cut lengthwise into slices

2   tablespoons crumbled blue cheese

¼   cup chopped walnuts

Dressing:

2   tablespoons balsamic vinegar

3   tablespoons extra-virgin olive oil

3   tablespoons orange juice

1   clove garlic, crushed

     Salt and freshly ground pepper, to taste

> **WHY IT'S GOOD FOR YOU:**
> * Antioxidants in spinach and pears
> * Good fat in olive oil and walnuts

In a salad bowl, place spinach, pears and cheese. Whisk together dressing ingredients and toss with salad. Toast walnuts 5 minutes in 325°F oven. Sprinkle warm walnuts over salad. Serve.

Serves 4.

Per serving: 243 calories, 17g total fat (2.6g saturated), 24g carbohydrate, 4g protein, 5.7g fiber, 93mg sodium.

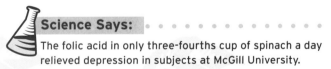

Science Says: The folic acid in only three-fourths cup of spinach a day relieved depression in subjects at McGill University.

Orange-Watercress Salad

1   **bunch watercress, cleaned and trimmed (4 to 5 cups)**

2   **medium Valencia oranges, peeled, thinly sliced, seeds removed**

¼   **cup chopped red onion**

Dressing:

2   **tablespoons extra-virgin olive oil**

2   **tablespoons balsamic vinegar**

2   **tablespoons orange juice**

   Salt and freshly ground black pepper, to taste

Put watercress, oranges and onions in a salad bowl. Combine oil, vinegar, orange juice, salt and freshly ground black pepper. Pour dressing over salad ingredients and toss.

Serves 6.

Substitutions: Instead of oranges, use grapefuit, avocado or mango slices, or 1 cup sliced strawberries or halved seedless grapes.

Per serving: 68 calories, 4.7g total fat (0.6g saturated), 7g carbohydrate, 1.2g protein, 1.3g fiber, 12mg sodium.

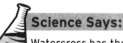

Science Says: • • • • • • • • • • • • • • • • •
Watercress has the highest overall antioxidant activity of any green leafy vegetable, including spinach.

• •

Romaine with Apples, Pecans and Blue Cheese Dressing

4½ cups hearts of romaine lettuce, torn into pieces

1 large unpeeled apple, such as Gala, chopped

1 Hass avocado, cubed

¼ cup toasted pecans, broken into pieces

½ cup chopped red onions

In a large bowl, combine salad ingredients.

Toss with ½ cup Creamy Blue Cheese Dressing, or more to taste.

Serves 4.

Per serving: Salad with dressing: 205 calories, 14g total fat (2.7g saturated), 17g carbohydrate, 5g protein, 3.8g fiber, 119mg sodium.

Creamy Blue Cheese Dressing

⅓ cup blue cheese (about 2.5 ounces)

2 tablespoons white vinegar

1 teaspoon Dijon mustard

⅓ cup orange juice

8 ounces plain fat-free yogurt

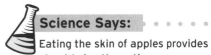

Science Says:

Eating the skin of apples provides about twice the anti-cancer activity as eating only the pulp, show Cornell University studies.

In a small bowl, mash cheese with a fork. Add vinegar, mustard, juice, yogurt; stir to combine thoroughly.

Makes 1½ cups.

Per 1 tablespoon: 18 calories, 0.8g total fat (0.5g saturated), 1g carbohydrate, 1g protein, 0g fiber, 53mg sodium

Mixed Greens with Beets, Oranges and Nutty Dressing

3 **medium beets (about 1½ pounds)**

4 **cups gourmet salad greens**

2 **oranges, peeled and sliced**

¼ **cup minced red onion**

¼ **cup feta cheese**

In a pot trim and scrub beets; cover with water and cook about 40 minutes. Rub off skins and remove tops. Cut beets into slices or julienne. Place salad greens on four plates. Top with beets, oranges, onions and cheese.

Drizzle 2 tablespoons of Blender Nut Dressing over each salad.

Serves 4.

Per serving with dressing: 261 calories, 17g total fat (3g saturated), 26g carbohydrate, 5g protein, 4.5g fiber, 304mg sodium.

Blender Nut Dressing

½ **cup chopped walnuts**

½ **cup extra-virgin olive oil**

¼ **cup balsamic vinegar**

¼ **cup orange juice**

Science Says:
Fruits and vegetables contain salicylic acid, aspirin's active compound. Vegetarians' blood has as much salicylic acid as that of aspirin-takers, enough to provide anti-inflammatory benefits.

Put all ingredients in a blender or food processor; process to desired smoothness.

Makes 1¼ cups.

Per tablespoon: 69 calories, 7.4g total fat (1g saturated), 1g carbohydrate, 0.5g protein, 0.1g fiber, 0mg sodium.

Mixed Greens with Figs and Walnuts

4 cups mixed gourmet greens

1 large fennel bulb, thinly sliced

½ cup chopped red onion

8 fresh ripe figs, cut in halves or quarters

½ cup walnut pieces

½ cup crumbled feta cheese

Dressing:

3 tablespoons extra-virgin olive oil

1½ tablespoons balsamic vinegar

1 clove garlic, crushed

3 tablespoons orange juice

Salt and freshly ground black pepper, to taste.

In a large bowl, combine salad ingredients and gently toss with dressing.

Serves 6.

Per serving: 235 calories, 15.8g total fat (3g saturated), 22g carbohydrate, 4.8g protein, 4.9g fiber, 159mg sodium.

WHY IT'S GOOD FOR YOU:

* High antioxidants in greens, onion, fennel, figs

* Good fat in olive oil and walnuts

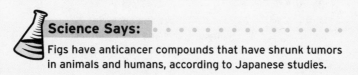

Science Says: • • • • • • • • • •
Figs have anticancer compounds that have shrunk tumors in animals and humans, according to Japanese studies.

Pear-Mint Salad with Parmesan Shavings

1   pear (preferably red), quartered, cored and cut into thin lengthwise slices

1½ tablespoons balsamic vinegar

1   cup mixed greens, such as mesclun

3   tablespoons shavings of Parmesan or Romano cheese

2   tablespoons chopped fresh mint

1   tablespoon chopped walnuts, optional

2   teaspoons extra-virgin olive oil

WHY IT'S GOOD FOR YOU:

* High antioxidants in greens and pears
* Mint is antibacterial
* **Plus:** Vinegar suppresses blood sugar rises

Marinate pear slices in balsamic vinegar 5 minutes, tossing to coat. Drain pears, reserving vinegar. On two salad plates, place equal amounts of greens. Top with pears, cheese, mint and optional nuts. Mix reserved vinegar with oil, drizzle over salad.

Serves 2.

Per serving: 140 calories, 7.9g total fat (2.4g saturated), 15g carbohydrate, 4.9g protein, 2.9g fiber, 185mg sodium.

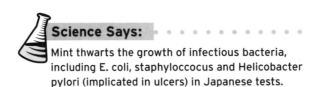

Science Says:

Mint thwarts the growth of infectious bacteria, including E. coli, staphyloccocus and Helicobacter pylori (implicated in ulcers) in Japanese tests.

Asparagus with Balsamic Dressing

24   medium stalks of green asparagus (about 1 pound)

 3   cups gourmet Italian salad greens with radicchio

¼   cup chopped hazelnuts

Dressing:

 6   tablespoons balsamic vinegar

 2   tablespoons extra-virgin olive oil

 2   teaspoons Dijon mustard

 1   teaspoons reduced-sodium soy sauce

 2   tablespoons orange juice

Whisk together all ingredients except hazelnuts.

Trim, peel and rinse asparagus: do not dry. Place spears flat two or three deep in a glass pie plate or similar dish. Cover *very tightly* with microwavable plastic wrap, and microwave on high 2½ minutes to 5 minutes, depending on wattage. Whisk together dressing ingredients; pour over asparagus and marinate in refrigerator until cool.

Divide greens onto four salad plates; top each with six asparagus spears. Drizzle with equal amounts of dressing and top with hazelnuts.

Serves 4.

Per serving: 149 calories, 11g total fat (1g saturated), 8g carbohydrate, 4g protein, 2g fiber, 137mg sodium.

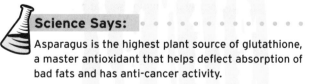

Science Says: • • • • • • • • • • • • • •
Asparagus is the highest plant source of glutathione, a master antioxidant that helps deflect absorption of bad fats and has anti-cancer activity.

• •

Antipasto Salad with Basil

- **3** tablespoons extra-virgin olive oil
- **1** tablespoon balsamic vinegar
- **2** cloves garlic, crushed or minced
- **1** 2-ounce can anchovies, chopped, optional
- **6** plum tomatoes, chopped
- **1** cup chopped red onion
- **½** cup black kalamata olives, chopped
- **1** cup basil leaves, torn into pieces
- **½** cup flat-leaf parsley chopped
  Freshly ground black pepper, to taste
- **⅓** cup crumbled feta cheese, optional

Pour olive oil and vinegar into a medium bowl; stir in garlic and optional anchovies. Add tomatoes, onion, olives, basil and parsley; toss. Divide among six plates; top with pepper and optional cheese.

Serves 6.

Per serving: 140 calories, 11.8g total fat (2.5g saturated), 8g carbohydrate, 2.3g protein, 2g fiber, 295mg sodium.

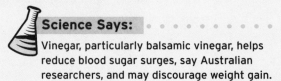

Science Says: Vinegar, particularly balsamic vinegar, helps reduce blood sugar surges, say Australian researchers, and may discourage weight gain.

Confetti Bean Salad

- 2 cups red cabbage, shredded
- 1 19-ounce can white (cannellini) beans, drained and rinsed
- 1 11-ounce can mandarin oranges, drained
- 1/3 cup walnuts, toasted
- 2 large scallions, sliced with green tops
- 3 tablespoons extra-virgin olive oil
- 2 tablespoons balsamic vinegar
- 2 tablespoons orange juice

  Salt and freshly ground black pepper, to taste

Put first five ingredients in a bowl. Whisk together oil, vinegar and juice. Toss all. Taste for seasoning. Serve.

Serves 6.

Per serving: 196 calories, 11g total fat (1g saturated), 19g carbohydrate, 5g protein, 5g fiber, 118mg sodium.

WHY IT'S GOOD FOR YOU:

* Anti-cancer compounds in cabbage
* Fiber in beans
* Antioxidants in oranges and scallions
* **Plus:** Beans help lower cholesterol and blood sugar.

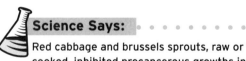

Science Says: • • • • • • • •
Red cabbage and brussels sprouts, raw or cooked, inhibited precancerous growths in laboratory animals in Austrian studies.

Orange White-Bean Salad

3 cups white cannellini beans, drained and rinsed

1 cup diced celery

1 cup chopped red onions

2 tablespoons each white wine vinegar and water

6 tablespoons orange juice concentrate

½ cup chopped fresh mint

½ teaspoon finely minced jalapeño pepper, optional

WHY IT'S GOOD FOR YOU:

* High fiber and high folic acid in beans

* Antioxidants in celery, red onions, orange juice

* **Plus:** Beans are very "low-glycemic," help control blood sugar and lower cholesterol

Combine all. Serve chilled or at room temperature.

Serves 5.

Per serving: 173 calories, 1g total fat (0.2g saturated), 32g carbohydrate, 10.7g protein, 5g fiber 236mg sodium.

Science Says: • • • • • • • • • • •
Orange juice is rich in the antioxidant hesperetin, which blocks specific enzymes from switching on cancer-causing agents in the body.

Black Beans with Mint and Feta

2　15-ounce cans black beans, rinsed and drained
　　(preferably no-salt added)*

½　cup chopped red onion

4　ounces feta cheese, crumbled

2　tablespoons extra-virgin olive oil

2　tablespoons fresh lemon juice

½　cup tightly packed fresh mint leaves, chopped

　　Salt and freshly ground pepper, to taste

Toss together all the ingredients.
Refrigerate 30 minutes before serving.

Serves 4.

Per serving: 278 calories, 14g total fat (5.3g saturated),
26g carbohydrate, 13g protein, 8.5g fiber, 672mg sodium.
*With no-salt added beans, the sodium drops to 353mg per serving

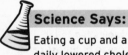

Science Says: • • • • • • • • • •
Eating a cup and a half of cooked dried beans
daily lowered cholesterol an average 19 percent
after three weeks in University of Kentucky tests.

• • • • • • • • • • • • • • • • • •

Thai Ginger-Cabbage Salad

Inspired by a salad at Spices Restaurant in Washington, D.C.

¾ **cup pickled ginger (in a 6-oz jar or fresh from an Asian market)**

4 **cups shredded green or red cabbage**

½ **cup peanuts, crushed**

¼ **cup mirin (sweetened rice wine)**

¼ **cup rice vinegar**

4 **scallions, sliced**

Combine all ingredients.

Serves 6.

Per serving: 178 calories, 6g total fat (0.8g saturated), 25g carbohydrate, 4g protein, 3g fiber, 198mg sodium.

WHY IT'S GOOD FOR YOU:

＊Anti-coagulant, antibiotic activity in ginger

＊Anti-cancer chemicals in cabbage

＊Plus peanuts help suppress blood sugar

Science Says: Cabbage and other cruciferous vegetables fed to lab animals reduced the incidence and spread of breast cancers.

Red Cabbage-Apple Slaw

4   cups red cabbage, shredded or sliced

2   apples, such as Gala, cored and diced

1/3 cup walnut pieces, toasted

Dressing:

1½ tablespoons extra-virgin olive oil

1½ tablespoons balsamic vinegar

1/3 cup frozen apple juice concentrate

Salt and freshly ground black pepper,
to taste

Combine cabbage, apples and walnuts. Whisk together
oil, vinegar, juice, salt and freshly ground black pepper
to make a dressing. Toss with cabbage mixture and serve
immediately or refrigerate.

Serves 6.

Per serving: 138 calories, 7.8g total fat (0.9g saturated),
18g carbohydrate, 1.8g protein, 2.7g fiber, 10mg sodium.

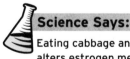

Science Says: • • • • • • • • • • • • •

Eating cabbage and other cruciferous vegetables
alters estrogen metabolism in ways that appear to
help prevent breast cancer and prostate cancer.

• •

Broccoli Slaw with Lemon Dressing

4 cups "broccoli slaw," available packaged in most produce sections

8 ounces fat-free lemon yogurt

1 tablespoon reduced-sodium soy sauce

¼ cup fresh lemon juice or white rice vinegar

¼ cup toasted sesame seeds

1 red apple, cored and chopped, optional

Toss all ingredients together and serve.

Serves 4.

Per serving: 143 calories, 5g total fat (1.7g saturated), 19g carbohydrate, 7g protein, 4g fiber, 306mg sodium.

WHY IT'S GOOD FOR YOU:

* Super antioxidants in broccoli

* Gut protecting-bacteria in yogurt

Science Says: Eating lots of broccoli, cabbage, kale, Brussels sprouts and cauliflower (brassica vegetables) reduces the risk of lung, stomach, colon and rectal cancer, studies find.

Sweet-and-Sour Cucumbers

2   large cucumbers, peeled and thinly sliced

3   scallions, thinly sliced, with 3 inches of green tops

²/₃ cup rice vinegar

¹/₃ cup sugar or no-calorie sweetener such as Splenda

Combine all ingredients; marinate for at least half an hour. With a slotted spoon, serve as a salad or a garnish.

Serves 4.

Per serving: 47 calories, 0.2g total fat, 12g carbohydrate, 0.7g protein, 1.2g fiber, 4mg sodium.

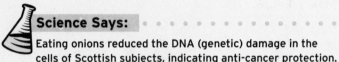

Science Says: Eating onions reduced the DNA (genetic) damage in the cells of Scottish subjects, indicating anti-cancer protection.

Cranberry-Fruit Sauce

1	12-ounce bag fresh cranberries
½	cup water
3	medium apples, such as Gala, peeled and chopped coarsely
2	pears, such as Bartlett, peeled and chopped coarsely
4-6	tablespoons sugar or no-calorie sweetener, such as Splenda
1½	tablespoons ground cinnamon
½	cup walnut pieces, optional

WHY IT'S GOOD FOR YOU:

* High antioxidants in cranberries and apples
* Plus cinnamon helps regulate blood sugar
* Cranberries help prevent urinary tract infections

Combine all ingredients except nuts, in a saucepan. Cover and simmer , stirring occasionally, until cranberries pop, 25-30 minutes. Cool to room temperature or chill. Stir in optional nuts. Makes 4 cups.

Serves 12.

Per serving: 66 calories, 0.3g total fat, 17g carbohydrate, 0.3g protein, 3g fiber, 0mg sodium.

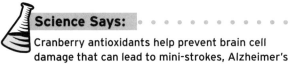

Science Says:
Cranberry antioxidants help prevent brain cell damage that can lead to mini-strokes, Alzheimer's and Parkinson's, find Tufts University researchers.

Carrot-Pineapple Salad

3   cups shredded or grated carrots (4 large carrots)

1   cup canned, crushed pineapple in juice

2   teaspoons fresh lemon juice or to taste

¼   cup chopped walnuts, optional

In a bowl, combine all ingredients and toss.

Serves 4.

Per serving: 73 calories, 0.2g total fat, 18g carbohydrate, 1g protein, 3g fiber, 30mg sodium

Science Says:

Eating five large carrots a week cut the risk of stroke by 68 percent in a large group of female nurses, compared with eating no carrots or only one a month.

More Good-For-You Low-Calorie Salad Dressings

Poppy Seed Dressing

1/2   cup firm tofu

1/4   cup frozen orange juice concentrate

1/4   cup rice vinegar

1   clove garlic, crushed

2   teaspoons fresh lemon juice

2   teaspoons poppy seeds

Combine all ingredients in a blender and process until smooth.

Makes 1 generous cup.

Per tablespoon: 20 calories, 0.9g total fat (0.1g saturated), 2g carbohydrate, 1.4g protein, 0g fiber, 2mg sodium.

Banana-Onion Dressing

2   large ripe bananas, peeled and cut into chunks

3/4   cup yellow onions, chopped

1/4   cup frozen unsweetened apple juice concentrate

Hot chili sauce to taste, optional

Salt and freshly ground pepper to taste

In a blender, process ingredients until smooth.

Makes about 2½ cups.

Per Tablespoon: 10 calories, 0g total fat, 3g carbohydrate, 0.2g fiber, 1mg sodium.

Minty-Lime Yogurt Dressing

6   ounce container fat-free key lime yogurt

1/4   cup fresh lime juice

1/4   cup chopped fresh mint leaves

Salt and freshly ground pepper to taste

In a blender, process all ingredients until smooth.

Makes about 1 cup.

Per tablespoon: 11 calories, 0 total fat, 2g carbohydrate, 0.4g protein, 0g fiber, 6mg sodium.

Tomato-Basil Dressing

3/4 cup tomato juice

10 large basil leaves, shredded

2 teaspoons fresh thyme or oregano

2 teaspoons prepared mustard

Salt and freshly ground pepper to taste

In a blender, process ingredients until basil is finely chopped.

Chill before serving.

Makes about 3/4 cup.

Per Tablespoon: 4 calories, 0g total fat, 1g carbohydrate, 0g protein, 0g fiber, 66mg sodium.

Creamy Garlic-Basil Dressing

1 cup fat-free plain yogurt

4 large cloves garlic, roughly chopped

1/3 cup tightly packed fresh basil leaves

2 teaspoons frozen orange juice concentrate, optional

Salt and freshly ground pepper to taste

In a blender, process all ingredients until smooth.

Makes about 1 1/4 cups.

Per tablespoon: 9 calories, 0g total fat, 1g carbohydrate, 1g protein, 0g fiber, 9mg sodium.

Tangy Avocado Dressing

1 ripe Hass avocado, cut into chunks

2 tablespoons white wine vinegar

3 tablespoons lemon juice

2 teaspoons Dijon mustard

1 cup fat-free half and half

Hot chili sauce to taste

Salt and freshly ground black pepper to taste

In a blender, process ingredients until smooth and creamy

Makes about 1 1/2 cups.

Per tablespoon: 18 calories, 1g total fat, 1g carbohydrate, 0g fiber, 18mg sodium.

Honey Ginger Dressing for Fruit

¾ cup fat-free vanilla yogurt

1 teaspoon honey

2 teaspoons minced crystallized ginger

⅛ teaspoon ground cumin

⅛ teaspoon cayenne pepper, or to taste

Whisk together all ingredients.

Makes about ¾ cup.

Per tablespoon: 16 calories, 0g total fat, 3g carbohydrate, 0.7g protein, 0g fiber, 10mg sodium.

Orange Yogurt Salad Dressing

½ cup fat-free plain yogurt

¼ teaspoon pure vanilla extract

1 teaspoon honey

2 tablespoons frozen orange juice concentrate

Whisk together all ingredients.

Makes ⅔ cup.

Per tablespoon: 14 calories, 0g total fat, 3g carbohydrate, 0.1g protein, 0g fiber, 9mg sodium.

Dr. Jim Duke's Sesame Seed Dressing

½ cup white wine vinegar

2 tablespoons dark sesame oil or olive oil

2 tablespoons reduced-sodium soy sauce

2 teaspoons grated fresh ginger

2 cloves garlic, chopped

¼ teaspoon hot red pepper flakes or to taste

2 tablespoons toasted sesame seeds.

In a blender process all ingredients, except sesame seeds, until smooth. Stir in sesame seeds and serve.

Makes about ¾ cup.

Per tablespoon: 32 calories, 3g total fat, 1g carbohydrate, 0g fiber, 101mg sodium.

Grilled Tuna with Avocado and Mango

1   **pound fresh tuna steak, 1 inch thick**

Sauce:

2   tablespoons extra-virgin olive oil

3   tablespoons fresh lime juice

    Grated zest of 2 limes

2   teaspoons reduced-sodium soy sauce

10 dashes hot sauce, such as Tabasco

    Salt and freshly ground black pepper, to taste

Salad ingredients:

3/4 cup thinly sliced scallions, with some green

3/4 cup diced red onions

2   Hass avocados, diced

1   mango, diced (or substitute 1 cup drained mandarin oranges)

1/4 cup chopped fresh cilantro or basil

Brush olive oil on both sides of tuna and on grill rack. Sear tuna about 2½ minutes on each side; it will be rare inside. Do not overcook. Remove and when cool, cut tuna into pieces, about 1-inch square. Optional: sear tuna in a heavy nonstick skillet, brushed with olive oil.

In a large bowl, whisk together olive oil, lime juice, zest, soy sauce, hot sauce, salt and pepper. Add grilled or seared tuna, scallions and onions, mix well and let sit for a few minutes. Add avocado and mango and toss lightly. Optional: heap tuna on a platter and surround with avocado and mango. Sprinkle with fresh herbs and serve at room temperature or chilled.

Serves 4.

Per serving: 425 calories, 27g total fat (4.7g saturated), 22g carbohydrate, 27g protein, 3.7g fiber, 177mg sodium.

Science Says:
Eating tuna, salmon and sardines at least once a week slowed artery clogging in women, according to Tufts University studies.

WHY IT'S GOOD FOR YOU:
* High omega-3 fat in tuna
* High potassium in avocado
* Antioxidants in onion, mango and herbs

Mixed Greens with Cumin-Crusted Salmon

Salad:

2   ounces pine nuts, toasted

5   cups mixed greens

1   15-ounce can black beans, drained and rinsed

1   cup sliced scallions

1   large orange, cut in 1-inch pieces

½   cup crumbled feta cheese

1   cup chopped fresh cilantro

Cumin-Crusted Salmon:

1½   tablespoons ground cumin

2   teaspoons paprika

Salt and freshly ground black pepper to taste

1   pound salmon fillet, skin removed

Dressing:

2   tablespoons orange juice concentrate

4   tablespoons extra-virgin olive oil

½   teaspoon ground cumin

1½   tablespoons balsamic vinegar

2   cloves garlic, crushed

Salt to taste

WHY IT'S GOOD FOR YOU:

* High omega-3 fat in salmon
* Antioxidants in greens, scallions, garlic and herbs
* Fiber and phytochemicals in beans
* Good fat in olive oil
* **Plus:** Cumin is anti-cancer and anti-inflammatory

In a large bowl, place all salad ingredients (reserve half of the cilantro and half of the pine nuts for garnish).

In a separate bowl, whisk together dressing ingredients.

In a shallow dish, combine cumin, paprika, salt and pepper. Cut salmon into 8 strips and coat with spices. Grill (or sear in a nonstick skillet brushed with canola oil) until crusty.

Toss salad and dressing; divide on plates. Top with salmon and reserved cilantro and pine nuts.

Serves 4.

Per serving: 583 calories, 37g total fat (8g saturated), 28g carbohydrate, 35g protein, 6.6g fiber, 683mg sodium.

Science Says:

The spice cumin is the richest source of a potent compound, farnesol, which suppresses pancreatic tumors in hamsters.

Low-Fat Taco Salad

4   corn tortillas (or substitute low-fat tortilla chips)

4   cups shredded dark green lettuce,such as romaine

½   cup chopped red onion

2   Hass avocados or 1 medium Florida avocado, cubed

1   4.5-ounce can chopped green chiles

1   large tomato, chopped

1½ cups tomato salsa

1   15-ounce can black beans, drained,
    rinsed (preferably no-salt-added)*

½   cup fat-free sour cream

1   cup shredded low-fat cheddar cheese

Preheat oven to 425°F. Spray tortillas on both sides with
canola oil. Cut into ½-inch-wide strips and spread on a
baking sheet. Bake, turning strips once, until brown and
crispy, about 8 minutes.

Combine lettuce, onion, avocado, chiles, and chopped tomato.
Combine salsa and beans. Divide salad on four plates.
Top with salsa mixture, cheese, sour cream and tortilla strips.

Serves 4.

Per serving: 423 calories, 17.4g total fat (5.4g saturated),
53g carbohydrate, 20g protein, 8g fiber, 1108mg sodium.
*With no-salt added beans, the sodium drops to 949mg per serving.

Science Says: • • • • • • • •
All dark green lettuces contain a variety of
antioxidants, including beta carotene and lutein.

• • • • • • • • • • • • • • • • • •

Salade Niçoise

5 ounces fresh baby spinach or large spinach leaves torn into bite-size pieces

1 12-ounce can water-packed light tuna, drained and separated into chunks

1 medium red onion, chopped

3/4 pound small red potatoes, cooked and quartered

1 10-ounce package frozen green beans, cooked, preferably French-cut

1½ cups grape tomatoes or halved cherry tomatoes

16 small black olives, preferably oil-cured

1/3 cup crumbled feta cheese

Freshly ground black pepper, to taste

Dressing:

½ cup extra-virgin olive oil

2 teaspoons Dijon mustard

2 cloves garlic, crushed

Salt to taste

3 tablespoons balsamic vinegar

Cover the bottom of a large, shallow salad bowl with spinach leaves. In another large bowl, whisk together dressing ingredients. Add tuna, potatoes, onion and green beans and toss to combine. Spoon mixture over spinach leaves. Decorate with tomatoes and olives, sprinkle on feta cheese. Top with freshly ground black pepper.

Serves 8 as luncheon salad.

Per serving: 260 calories, 16.5g total fat (1.2g saturated), 15g carbohydrate, 14g protein, 2.6g fiber, 238mg sodium.

WHY IT'S GOOD FOR YOU:

* Antioxidants in spinach, onions, green beans, tomatoes, olives, garlic

* Good omega-3 fat in tuna

* Plus olive oil eaters have less chronic disease

Science Says:

Greeks who eat a Mediterranean-style diet – high in fish, vegetables, olive oil and salads – have lower blood levels of inflammation, fibrinogen and homocysteine, which are all risk factors for heart disease.

Classic "Stone-Age" Salad

5 cups mixed greens, such as mesclun, spinach or dark green lettuce

1½ cups cooked garbanzo beans (chick peas)

½ cup red onion, chopped or in rings

1 cup cooked chicken breast cubes

1 cup chopped cauliflower

½ cup walnut pieces

3 tablespoons chopped fresh herbs, such as parsley, basil or cilantro

Dressing:

6 tablespoons orange juice

2 teaspoons balsamic vinegar

2 tablespoons canola oil or extra-virgin olive oil

2 cloves garlic, crushed

Salt and freshly ground pepper, to taste

In a large bowl, combine salad ingredients.
In a small bowl, whisk dressing. Toss together.

Serves 4.

Per serving: 331 calories, 19.3g total fat (1.8g saturated), 22g carbohydrate, 9.5g protein, 6g fiber, 182mg sodium.

WHY IT'S GOOD FOR YOU:

✳ Antioxidants in spinach, onion, cauliflower, walnuts, herbs, orange juice, garlic

✳ Fiber and phytochemicals in garbanzo beans

✳ Good protein, low fat in chicken breast

Science Says:

Eating greens, legumes, nuts and low-fat animal protein, such as chicken, is more compatible with our ancient "stone-age" genes and more apt to promote health.

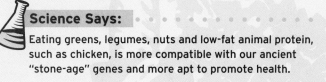

Fruity Chicken Curry Salad

2   cups cooked chicken in bite-size pieces
1   20-ounce can chunk pineapple, drained
½   cup chopped celery
¼   cup fat-free sour cream
2   teaspoons curry powder
    Salt and freshly ground black pepper, to taste

Combine all.

Serves 4.

Per serving: 224 calories, 5.4g total fat (1.4g saturated), 22g carbohydrate, 22g protein, 87mg sodium.

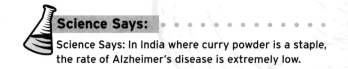

Science Says: • • • • • • • • • • •
Science Says: In India where curry powder is a staple, the rate of Alzheimer's disease is extremely low.

Jean's Super-Nutritious Entrée Salad

Here's how to get your daily quota of fruits and vegetables in one gigantic salad for lunch or dinner

1   cup romaine, in bite-size pieces

1   cup fresh spinach, in bite-size pieces

½   cup cauliflower pieces

½   cup chopped or thinly sliced red onion

½   cup shredded red cabbage

1   orange, peeled and sliced

½   cup strawberries

½   cup cooked garbanzo beans (chick peas)

2   tablespoons dry-roasted unsalted peanuts

¼   cup crumbled blue cheese or feta

2   ounces cooked chicken or turkey white meat, salmon, tofu or 1 hard-boiled egg, optional

Ginger Citrus Dressing

½   cup orange juice

2   tablespoons rice or white vinegar

2   tablespoons extra-virgin olive oil.

2   cloves garlic, crushed

1   teaspoon reduced sodium soy sauce,

1   teaspoon grated fresh ginger

¾   teaspoon ground cumin

Whisk dressing ingredients together in a small bowl.

Makes ¾ cup or 12 tablespoons.

In a very large bowl, toss salad ingredients with ¼ cup Ginger Citrus Dressing. Serve on a large plate.

Serves 1.

Per serving: 630 calories, 30.4g total fat (9.1g saturated), 73g carbohydrate, 25g protein, 18g fiber, 615 mg sodium.

WHY IT'S GOOD FOR YOU:

✳ Contains your daily quota of 8 servings of antioxidant-packed, anti-cancer fruits and vegetables

✳ High fiber – 18 grams

✳ Lots of nutrients for few calories

✳ Good fat in olive oil

✳ Plus: Ginger is anti-inflammatory

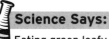

Science Says: • • • • • • • • • • • • • • •

Eating green leafy vegetables, beans, olive oil, nuts and multigrain bread – in short, wholesome foods – leads to smoother skin and fewer wrinkles when you are older, find Australian rsearchers.

• •

Green Bean Casserole

1	16-ounce package frozen green beans, French cut
½	cup fat-free cottage cheese
½	cup (about 3 ounces) chèvre (soft goat cheese) with garlic and herbs
½	cup toasted slivered almonds
¼	cup freshly grated Parmesan cheese
	Freshly ground black pepper, to taste

WHY IT'S GOOD FOR YOU:
* Antioxidants in green beans and almonds
* Low saturated fat
* Low calorie

Preheat oven to 375°F. Cook green beans according to package directions and drain. In a blender, mix cottage cheese and chèvre. Combine green beans, blended cheeses and almonds; turn into a baking dish. Top with Parmesan cheese and pepper. Bake for 20 minutes. To brown top, put under a broiler for 3-5 minutes.

Serves 6.

Per serving: 161 calories, 10g total fat (3.4g saturated), 9g carbohydrate, 10g protein, 2g fiber, 205mg sodium.

Science Says: Colon cancer risk decreases when you eat lots of green vegetables, according to numerous studies.

Stir-Fry Broccoli with Orange Sauce

1   teaspoon sesame oil

1   teaspoon canola oil

2   cups bite-size broccoli florets

½   cup orange juice

2   teaspoons cornstarch

1   tablespoon reduced-sodium soy sauce

½   teaspoon no-calorie sweetener
    such as Splenda or sugar

⅓   cup walnuts, toasted

WHY IT'S GOOD FOR YOU:

✳ Super antioxidants in broccoli

✳ Anti-cancer chemicals in orange juice

✳ Good fat and fiber in walnuts

✳ Low saturated fat

In a small skillet, heat oils over medium-high heat.
Add broccoli and stir-fry about 3-5 minutes. Combine orange juice,
cornstarch and soy sauce and optional sweetener. Add mixture
to broccoli; lower heat and cook until sauce is thickened, about
1 minute. Stir in walnuts and serve.

Serves 2.

Per serving: 252 calories, 16g total fat (1.5g saturated), 9g protein,
19g carbohydrate, 4g fiber, 345mg sodium.

Science Says: • • • • • • • • • • • • •

Broccoli's main chemical, sulforaphane, performs
wonders in preventing cancer in animals – slashing
incidence by 60 percent and size by 75 percent.

• •

Low-Fat Creamed Spinach

2   small cloves garlic, crushed or minced

1   tablespoon extra-virgin olive oil

1   10-ounce package frozen chopped spinach,
    thawed and squeezed dry

¼   cup fat-free cream cheese

¼   cup fat-free half-and-half

    Salt and freshly ground black pepper, to taste

    Dash of ground nutmeg

WHY IT'S GOOD FOR YOU:

* Super antioxidants in spinach and garlic

* Low saturated fat

* Low calorie

In a small skillet, sauté garlic in olive oil until soft but not brown; add spinach, cream cheese and half-and-half. Cook, stirring, until blended and heated through, about 5 minutes. Stir in salt, pepper and nutmeg and serve.

Serves 4.

Per serving: 71 calories, 3.7g total fat (0.5g saturated), 5.6g carbohydrate, 4g protein, 1.5g fiber, 135mg sodium.

Science Says: • • • • • • • • • • • •

Women who eat the most spinach and other greens lower odds of breaking a hip by 30 percent. Leafy greens are high in bone-protecting vitamin K.

Scalloped Corn with Peppers

1 **16-ounce package frozen yellow corn kernels***

1 **4-ounce can chopped green chiles**

2 **eggs or ½ cup egg substitute**

1 **cup fat-free half-and-half**

1 **tablespoon butter or trans-free margarine**

¾ **cup crushed low-fat tortilla chips**

Salt and freshly ground black pepper, to taste

WHY IT'S GOOD FOR YOU:

*Antioxidants in corn and chiles

*Choline and lutein in eggs

Preheat oven to 400°F. Combine all ingredients. Put in a casserole; cover and bake 20 minutes. Remove cover and bake 15 more minutes, or until browned.

Serves 6.

Per serving: 205 calories, 9.5g total fat (4.6g saturated), 27g carbohydrate, 6.8g protein, 2.6g fiber, 194mg sodium.

Note: frozen corn is much lower in sodium than canned corn.

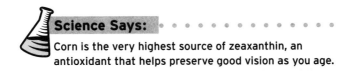

Science Says: • • • • • • • • • • • •

Corn is the very highest source of zeaxanthin, an antioxidant that helps preserve good vision as you age.

Beets with Orange and Ginger

6   medium beets

1   tablespoon cornstarch

1   cup orange juice

1   tablespoon white vinegar

2   tablespoons maple syrup

2   tablespoons chopped crystallized ginger

½   cup walnut pieces

Scrub beets, leaving on root and 1 inch of stem. Place beets in a large pot with water to cover. Bring to a boil, cover and simmer about 45 to 60 minutes or until tender. Drain, rub off skins (or peel) and cut into wedges.

In a saucepan combine cornstarch, orange juice, maple syrup, vinegar, ginger and walnuts. Bring to a boil and simmer until sauce has thickened. Add beets and toss to coat.

Serves 6.

Per serving: 193 calories, 6g total fat (0.6g saturated), 32g carbohydrate, 4g protein, 2.3g fiber, 121mg sodium

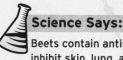

Science Says:
Beets contain anti-cancer chemicals that inhibit skin, lung, and liver tumors in mice.

Portobellos Stuffed with Greens and Cheese

1   10-ounce package frozen collard greens or kale
(about 2½ cups cooked)

2½ tablespoons extra-virgin olive oil

1½ tablespoons fresh lemon juice

2   large cloves garlic, crushed

1½ teaspoons dried thyme leaves

4   portobello mushrooms, stems removed

4   ounces Brie cheese, rind removed

    Salt and freshly ground black pepper, to taste

WHY IT'S GOOD FOR YOU:

* Super antioxidant (lutein) in collard greens
* Antioxidants in garlic and thyme
* **Plus:** Portobello mushrooms have anti-cancer activity

Preheat oven to 350°F. Microwave greens using package directions; drain and squeeze dry. Combine greens, oil, lemon juice, garlic, thyme and salt. Put mushrooms, stem-side up, in a baking dish. Fill hollows with greens. Top each with ¼ of the cheese and freshly ground black pepper. Bake 10 minutes. Broil to brown cheese, 2 minutes.

Serves 4.

Per serving: 228 calories, 17.1g total fat (1.3g saturated), 12g carbohydrate, 11g protein, 3g fiber, 220mg sodium.

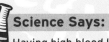

Science Says: · · · · · · · · · · · · · · · · · ·
Having high blood lutein from eating kale, spinach and broccoli, slowed thickening of neck arteries and stopped the progression of artery clogging in a University of Southern California study.

Oregano-Baked Onions

4   medium yellow onions, peeled but not sliced

¼   cup balsamic vinegar

½   cup white wine, broth or water

2   teaspoons dried oregano

¼   teaspoon salt

    Freshly ground black pepper, to taste

Preheat oven to 425°F. Place onions upright in baking dish sprayed with oil. Mix vinegar, wine and seasonings; pour over onions. Bake, covered, until onions are tender, about 45 minutes.

Serves 4.

Per serving: 72 calories, 0.6g total fat, 16g carbohydrate, 2g protein, 2.7g fiber, 150mg sodium.

Science Says:

Onions have potent antibacterial activity, destroying many disease-causing pathogens, including E. coli and salmonella.

Broccoli-Cauliflower Roast

2   cups broccoli florets, 1 to 2 inches in diameter

2   cups cauliflower florets, 1 to 2 inches in diameter

5   cloves garlic, peeled and halved

2   tablespoons extra-virgin olive oil

    Salt and freshly ground black pepper, to taste

1   teaspoon grated Parmesan cheese

Preheat oven to 450°F. Toss broccoli, cauliflower and garlic with olive oil. Spread on a baking sheet and bake for 20 minutes, or until browned and tender-crunchy. Stir once or twice. Season to taste with salt and pepper. Sprinkle with Parmesan cheese before serving.

Serves 4.

Per serving: 92 calories, 7.2g total fat (1g saturated), 6g carbohydrate, 3g protein, 2.3g fiber, 37mg sodium.

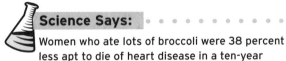

Science Says: • • • • • • • • • • •
Women who ate lots of broccoli were 38 percent less apt to die of heart disease in a ten-year study of 35,000 older women in Iowa.

Quick Peanut Cabbage

4 **cups thinly sliced cabbage**

2 **tablespoons chunky peanut butter, preferably natural**

2 **tablespoons frozen orange or apple juice concentrate**

2 **tablespoons balsamic vinegar**

¼ **teaspoon hot pepper flakes or to taste**

Put all the ingredients in a microwave-safe bowl. Cover and microwave on high for 4 minutes, or until the cabbage is limp and the peanut butter has melted. Stir to coat the cabbage with sauce and serve.

Serves 6.

Per serving: 54 calories, 2.8g total fat (0.5g saturated), 6g carbohydrate, 2g protein, 1.3g fiber, 11mg sodium.

WHY IT'S GOOD FOR YOU:

* Anti-cancer chemicals in cabbage
* Antioxidants in orange juice
* **Plus:** Peanut butter helps control blood sugar and suppress appetite.

Science Says: Eating cabbage and sauerkraut may slow estrogen activity and growth of estrogen-stimulated human breast cancer cells, discouraging cancer spread, according to University of Illinois research.

*Fresh Spring
Rolls with Thai
Dipping Sauce
Page 63

* **Curried Lentil Soup**
Page 70

✳ Spinach and
Berries with
Curry Dressing
Page 84

*Asparagus
with
Balsamic
Dressing
Page 93

Portobellos Stuffed with Greens and Cheese
Page 119

*Quick Tex-Mex
Rice Casserole
Page 131

✳Hot Pepper Quesadillas
Page 132

*Pepper, Onion
& Feta Pizza
Page 142

Ziti Spinach Alfredo
Page 145

**❋Fiesta Seafood
Cassserole**
Page 159

*Gingery Fish
Kabobs with
Pineapple
Page 162

Salmon with Scalloped Sweet Potatoes
Page 168

**Greek-style
Turkey Burgers**
Page 186

Three-Berry Trifle
Page 196

Chocolate Cake with Raspberry Sauce
Page 198

＊Saucy Summer Fruit Salad
Page 211

Sweet Potato Puff

3½ pounds sweet potatoes (4 large)

½ cup orange marmalade or apricot preserves

¼ cup brown sugar, or to taste

½ cup orange juice

2 teaspoons pure almond extract

3 egg whites

2 tablespoons almond slivers, toasted lightly

Cook sweet potatoes until tender (15-20 minutes in a microwave, 1 hour in a 450°F-oven or boiled for 25 minutes). Let cool.

Preheat oven to 350°F. Peel sweet potatoes, place in a large bowl and mash. Add marmalade, sugar, orange juice and almond extract; beat with mixer until smooth. In a separate bowl, beat egg whites to stiff peaks. Fold into potato mixture. Coat a 6-cup casserole with nonstick spray. Add sweet potato mixture and sprinkle with almonds. Bake until puffy and set, about 40 minutes.

Serves 6.

Per serving: 340 calories, 2g total fat (0.2g saturated), 76g carbohydrate, 6g protein, 6g fiber, 71mg sodium.

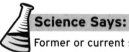

Science Says: • • • • • • • • •
Former or current smokers who ate a half cup of sweet potatoes, carrots or winter squash daily had half the lung cancer risk as those who ate none, says National Cancer Institute research.

• • • • • • • • • • • • • • • • • •

Warm Mapled Carrots with Walnuts

4 **cups carrots (1 pound),
cut into ¼-½-inch slices**

1 **tablespoon trans-fat-free margarine
or butter.**

2 **tablespoons maple syrup**

2 **tablespoons orange juice**

¼ **cup chopped walnuts, toasted
Dash of cinnamon, or to taste**

¼ **cup dried cranberries, optional**

2 **tablespoons chopped parsley for garnish,
optional**

In a medium saucepan, place carrots and ¾ cup water. Bring to a boil; cover and simmer until tender, about 15 minutes. Drain; place carrots in a large bowl. Add margarine or butter, maple syrup, orange juice, walnuts, and, if desired, cranberries. Toss. Serve warm, garnished with parsley.

Serves 8.

Per serving: 73 calories, 3.5g total fat (0.5 saturated), 10g carbohydrate, 1g protein, 2g fiber, 32 mg sodium.

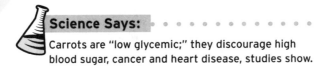

Science Says: • • • • • • • • • • •
Carrots are "low glycemic;" they discourage high blood sugar, cancer and heart disease, studies show.
• •

Mediterranean Grilled Vegetables

1   small eggplant (or half of medium), cut into chunks

1   medium red onion, cut into wedges

5   ounces portobello mushroom,
    cut into 1-inch slices

2   small bell peppers (1 red, 1 green),
    cut into chunks or slivers

2   cups cherry or grape tomatoes

Marinade:

6   tablespoons extra-virgin olive oil

2   tablespoons balsamic vinegar

1   tablespoon reduced-sodium soy sauce

2   cloves garlic, crushed

¼   cup chopped fresh rosemary or basil

**WHY IT'S GOOD
FOR YOU:**

＊Antioxidants in
eggplant, onion,
peppers and
tomatoes

＊Anti-cancer
chemicals in
mushrooms

＊Good fat in
olive oil

Prepare vegetables. Whisk together marinade ingredients in a large bowl. Add vegetables and toss to coat. Marinate 1 hour. Put vegetables (except tomatoes) in grilling basket or on skewers. Grill, brushing with marinade and turning several times, 15 minutes. Add tomatoes and grill 5 minutes longer, or until all vegetables are as tender as desired.

Serves 6.

Per serving: 168 calories, 14.4g total fat (2g saturated), 11g carbohydrate, 2.1g protein, 2.5g fiber, 180mg sodium.

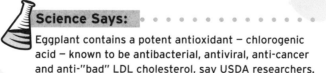

Science Says: • • • • • • • • • • • • • • • •
Eggplant contains a potent antioxidant – chlorogenic acid – known to be antibacterial, antiviral, anti-cancer and anti-"bad" LDL cholesterol, say USDA researchers.

• •

Curried Root Vegetables with Pineapple

4   cups assorted root vegetables
     (sweet potatoes, carrots, turnips and/or parsnips),
     cut into 1-inch chunks.

1   medium yellow onion, cut into 8 wedges

1   tablespoon curry powder

1   8-ounce can pineapple chunks in juice
     Freshly ground black pepper, to taste
     Fat-free plain yogurt, chopped cilantro
     and/or crushed peanuts, for garnish, optional

WHY IT'S GOOD FOR YOU:

* Antioxidants in root vegetables, onions and pineapple
* Plus: Curry powder has anti-inflammatory and anti-cancer activity

In a large microwave-safe bowl, combine all vegetables, curry and pineapple chunks with juice, cover tightly and microwave on high about 20-25 minutes or until vegetables are tender. Grind on fresh black pepper. Serve immediately. Top with optional yogurt, cilantro and peanuts if desired. You can also serve over brown rice.

Serves 6 a side dish, 4 as a main course.

Per side dish serving: 91 calories, 0.4g total fat, 22g carbohydrate, 1.6g protein, 3.8g fiber, 28mg sodium.

Science Says: . . . .

Sweet potatoes were first and carrots second among 58 vegetables in vitamins A and C, folate, iron, copper, calcium and fiber, as ranked by the Center for Science in the Public Interest.

Succotash with Orange

1   **10-ounce package frozen baby lima beans**

1   **cup frozen yellow corn kernels**

1   **cup orange juice**

3   **tablespoons rice vinegar or white wine vinegar**

1½ **cups shredded raw red cabbage**

Combine first four ingredients in a large microwave-safe bowl. Cover and microwave on high 8 minutes or until vegetables are cooked. Stir in cabbage. Serve warm or chilled.

Serves 6.

Per serving: 105 calories, 0.3g total fat, 23g carbohydrate, 4.6g protein, 3.8g fiber, 12mg sodium.

WHY IT'S GOOD FOR YOU:

✳ High fiber in beans

✳ Antioxidants in corn, orange juice and cabbage

✳ **Plus:** Beans hold down blood sugar rises

Science Says: ⋅ ⋅ ⋅ ⋅ ⋅ ⋅ ⋅ ⋅ ⋅ ⋅ ⋅
Foods such as beans that are low glycemic index (suppress blood sugar) are linked to a lower risk of colorectal cancer, says new Harvard research.

Herbed Grilled Tomatoes

1   tablespoon extra-virgin olive oil

2   medium tomatoes, halved crosswise

2   teaspoons Dijon mustard

¼   cup bread crumbs

2   teaspoons freshly grated Parmesan cheese

4   large basil leaves, shredded

1   teaspoon fresh thyme, oregano or rosemary
    or ¼ teaspoon dried

Freshly ground black pepper, to taste

Brush half of oil over sides and bottoms of tomatoes. Brush tops with mustard. Combine cheese, bread crumbs, herbs; sprinkle on top of tomatoes. Drizzle on rest of oil to dampen bread-crumb topping. Add pepper.

Put tomatoes on grill cut-side up; cover. Grill until skins shrink from top of tomatoes and tomatoes are soft but not mushy, 10-20 minutes, depending on heat of grill.

(Alternatively, roast in a 450°F-oven 15-20 minutes or broil 5-10 minutes.)

Serves 4.

Per serving: 75 calories, 4.4g total fat (0.8g saturated), 8g carbohydrate, 2g protein, 1.2g fiber, 112mg sodium.

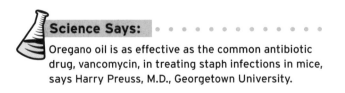

Science Says: • • • • • • • • • • • •

Oregano oil is as effective as the common antibiotic drug, vancomycin, in treating staph infections in mice, says Harry Preuss, M.D., Georgetown University.

• • • • • • • • • • • • • • • • • • •

Grilled Peppers

4 large bell peppers (red, green and/or yellow),
cored and cut lengthwise into 1-inch-wide strips

2 tablespoons extra-virgin olive oil

Heat grill. Toss peppers with olive oil.
Spread peppers on grill; cover grill if possible.
Cook until peppers are thoroughly limp
and slightly charred. Serve as a side dish
or as a topping for bread or polenta.

Serves 4.

Per serving: 87 calories, 7g total fat (1g saturated),
6g carbohydrate, 1g protein, 1.6g fiber, 2mg sodium.

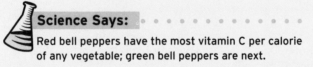

Science Says: Red bell peppers have the most vitamin C per calorie of any vegetable; green bell peppers are next.

Sweet and Sour Red Cabbage

½   **cup raisins**

½   **cup apple juice**

½   **large head red cabbage, coarsely shredded or sliced**

2   **tablespoons balsamic vinegar**

1   **tablespoon honey**

¼   **teaspoon ground cinnamon**

½   **cup chopped pecans, optional**

Soak the raisins in the apple juice for 2 hours or until plumped. Place the cabbage in a large microwave-safe bowl. Add vinegar and stir. Cover and microwave on high for about 5 minutes. Add raisins, apple juice, honey, cinnamon and mix. Microwave, covered, on high for 3 to 5 minutes more. The cabbage should still be slightly crunchy. Sprinkle with pecans and serve.

Serves 4.

Per serving: 125 calories, 0.5g total fat, 31g carbohydrate, 2.6g protein, 3.8g fiber, 19mg sodium.

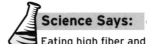

Science Says:

Eating high fiber and lots of fruits and vegetables lowers risk of colon polyps that can lead to cancer, says new National Cancer Institute research.

Quick Tex-Mex Rice Casserole

- **2** cups cooked brown rice
- **1½** cups tomato salsa
- **1** teaspoon chili powder
- **1** 15-ounce can no-salt-added black beans, not drained
- **1** cup frozen yellow corn kernels
- **2** ounces reduced-fat sharp Cheddar cheese, sliced ¼ inch thick
- **2** tablespoons sliced black or green olives, optional

WHY IT'S GOOD FOR YOU:

* Antioxidants in tomatoes and corn
* Fiber in beans
* **Plus:** Brown rice is whole grain, tied to less chronic disease

Combine rice, salsa, chili powder, black beans and corn. Spoon into a 6-by-6-inch, shallow, microwave-safe casserole. Top with cheese slices, then olives. Microwave on high for 12 minutes, until heated through and cheese is melted.

Serves 4.

Per serving: 298 calories, 3.8g total fat (2g saturated), 51g carbohydrate, 17g protein, 8g fiber, 674mg sodium.

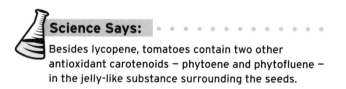

Science Says:
Besides lycopene, tomatoes contain two other antioxidant carotenoids – phytoene and phytofluene – in the jelly-like substance surrounding the seeds.

Hot Pepper Quesadillas

2	large (10-inch) flour tortillas, preferably whole wheat
1½	cups (6 ounces) "light" shredded jalapeño or "Mexican" cheese, such as Sargento Light Mexican
1	cup minced red onions
⅓	cup canned sliced jalapeño peppers, drained
¼	cup oil-cured black olives, pitted and sliced
1	cup shredded fresh spinach

Preheat oven to 425°F. On a pizza pan or cookie sheet, place one tortilla. Sprinkle with half of the cheese, followed by all the onions, jalapeños, olives and spinach. Top with the second tortilla. Sprinkle with remaining cheese. Bake 8-10 minutes, until cheese is melted and browned.

Let cool 5 minutes. Cut into 8 wedges and serve warm. Garnish with salsa, fat-free sour cream, minced onions, chopped cilantro, avocado slices or guacamole.

Makes 8 wedges.

Per wedge: 120 calories, 5.7g total fat (2.5g saturated), 10g carbohydrate, 7.8g protein, 1g fiber, 342mg sodium.

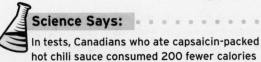

Science Says: In tests, Canadians who ate capsaicin-packed hot chili sauce consumed 200 fewer calories a few hours later than non-hot sauce eaters.

Moroccan Vegetable Delight

1 cup bulgur wheat

1 cup boiling water

1 medium yellow or red onion, chopped

1 tablespoon extra-virgin olive oil

2 large carrots, sliced into medium rounds

½ cup orange juice

1 15-ounce can garbanzo beans (chick peas), drained and rinsed

3 tablespoons honey

2½ teaspoons ground cumin

⅓ cup slivered almonds, toasted

¼ cup raisins or currants

WHY IT'S GOOD FOR YOU:

*Antioxidants in carrots, onion, orange juice, raisins

*Fiber in chick peas and raisins

*Good fat in olive oil

*Antibiotics in honey

*Plus: Bulgur wheat is whole grain, tied to less heart disease, less obesity and longer life

Pour bulgur into a small bowl. Add boiling water and set aside to soak for 30 minutes. Sauté onion in olive oil until soft. Simmer or microwave carrots in orange juice until tender. In a bowl, combine all ingredients. Warm in a microwave or serve at room temperature.

Serves 6.

Per serving: 316 calories, 8.7g total fat (0.8g saturated), 53g carbohydrate, 10g protein, 10g fiber, 159mg sodium.

Science Says:
Kids with low blood levels of beta and alpha carotene, found in carrots, and vitamin C, in orange juice, are at higher risk of asthma, studies show.

Spinach Chickpea Curry

1   tablespoon canola oil

1   tablespoon curry powder

1   cup chopped yellow onion

2   cloves garlic, crushed

10   ounces frozen chopped spinach, thawed, drained

1   8-ounce can tomato sauce

1   19-ounce can chick peas (garbanzo beans),
     drained and rinsed

1   cup fat-free, reduced-sodium vegetable
     or chicken broth

     Salt and freshly ground black pepper, to taste

     Hot sauce or red pepper flakes, to taste, optional

In a large skillet or saucepan, add oil, curry powder, onions and garlic; sauté about 5 minutes. Add spinach, tomato sauce and 1 cup of the chick peas. In a blender, puree remaining chick peas with broth. Add to vegetables. Simmer until heated through, about 10 minutes. Stir in seasonings. Serve over cooked brown rice or couscous.

Serves 4.

Per serving: 183 calories, 6g total fat (0.4g saturated), 26g carbohydrate, 8g protein, 7g fiber, 609mg sodium.

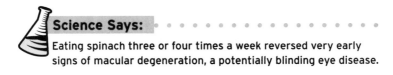

Science Says: Eating spinach three or four times a week reversed very early signs of macular degeneration, a potentially blinding eye disease.

Sweet Potato Stew with Black Beans

1   medium yellow onion, chopped (about 1 cup)

1   tablespoon chili powder

1   cup orange juice

1   tablespoon honey

   Salt, to taste

2   large sweet potatoes (about 2 pounds), peeled and cut into 1-inch chunks

1   15-ounce can black beans, drained and rinsed

2   teaspoons butter, softened

2   teaspoons flour

1/4   cup toasted almond slivers, optional

Put onions, chili powder, orange juice, honey, salt and sweet potatoes in a large, microwave-safe bowl. Cover and microwave on high power, stirring once, about 20 minutes or until potatoes are done but still hold their shape. Add beans. Blend butter and flour and add to the mixture. Microwave on high 5 minutes or until beans are heated through and stew has thickened slightly. Sprinkle with almonds, if desired.

Serves 6.

Per serving: 212 calories, 2g total fat (0.9g saturated), 44g carbohydrate, 5.2g protein, 6g fiber, 156mg sodium.

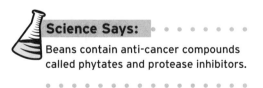

Science Says: • • • • • • •

Beans contain anti-cancer compounds called phytates and protease inhibitors.

"Meaty" Portobello Stew

12 ounces portobello mushrooms,
cut into bite-size pieces

2 tablespoons canola oil

1½ cups canned black bean soup
(use smooth, condensed soup;
if beans are whole, run through a blender)

1 14.5-ounce can fat-free,
reduced-sodium vegetable broth

1 large baking potato, in chunks

1½ cups carrots, small or cut

2 medium yellow onions, quartered

2 bay leaves

½ teaspoon dried thyme

½ cup red wine, optional

Salt and freshly ground black pepper, to taste

**WHY IT'S GOOD
FOR YOU:**

* Antioxidants in
carrots, onions
and herbs

* High fiber and
anti-cholesterol
activity in beans

* High potassium
in potato

* Plus: Portobello
mushrooms are
anti-cancer

Sauté mushrooms in oil until brown and softened, about 5 minutes;
set aside. In a large pot, combine bean soup, broth, potatoes,
carrots, onions and seasonings; simmer until vegetables are done,
about 20-30 minutes. Add mushrooms and red wine, if using.
Heat through. Season with salt and pepper. Serve with brown rice.

Serves 6.

Per serving: 147 calories, 22g carbohydrate, 4.6g protein, 4.5g fiber,
5.2g total fat (0.5g saturated), 626mg sodium.

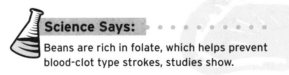

Science Says:

Beans are rich in folate, which helps prevent
blood-clot type strokes, studies show.

Mediterranean Vegetable Stew

2 tablespoons extra-virgin olive oil

1 cup chopped red onions

1 cup coarsely chopped green pepper

2 large cloves garlic, crushed

1 cup sliced white button mushrooms

1 small eggplant (unpeeled), cut into 1 to 2-inch chunks
   (about 12 ounces or 4 cups)

1 28-ounce can crushed tomatoes

1 15-ounce can chick peas (garbanzo beans),
   drained and rinsed

½ cup kalamata olives, pitted and sliced

1 tablespoon chopped fresh rosemary

1 cup coarsely chopped fresh parsley

⅓ cup crumbled feta cheese, optional

In a large skillet, heat 1 tablespoon of the olive oil. Sauté onions and green pepper until softened, stirring occasionally, about 10 minutes. Add the remaining 1 tablespoon olive oil, the garlic, mushrooms and eggplant. Simmer, stirring occasionally, until eggplant is softened, but not mushy, about 15 minutes. Add tomatoes, chick peas, olives and rosemary. Simmer until heated through, about 10 minutes. Turn off heat and stir in parsley. Sprinkle with feta cheese, if desired. Serve over brown rice, polenta, or couscous.

Serves 6.

Per serving: 191 calories, 9g total fat (1g saturated), 24g carbohydrate, 5.6g protein, 6g fiber, 507mg sodium.

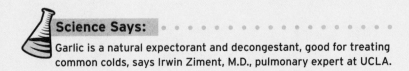

Science Says:

Garlic is a natural expectorant and decongestant, good for treating common colds, says Irwin Ziment, M.D., pulmonary expert at UCLA.

Dr. Jenkins' Greek Bean Stew

Adapted from a recipe by diabetes researcher David Jenkins, University of Toronto.

3   **large cloves garlic, minced**

2   **cups chopped onions**

1   **green pepper, diced**

2   **tablespoons extra-virgin olive oil**

1   **28-ounce can crushed tomatoes**

4   **cups white beans (navy, pea or cannellini),
      drained and rinsed**

2   **bay leaves**

1   **teaspoon dried oregano**

    Dash hot chili sauce

½   **cup pitted black Greek olives, preferably kalamata**

**WHY IT'S GOOD
FOR YOU:**

* Antioxidants in
   tomatoes, garlic,
   onions, pepper,
   olives

* High fiber in
   beans

* Antibiotics in
   oregano

In a large pot, sauté garlic, onions and pepper in oil until soft, about 10 minutes. Add tomatoes, beans, bay leaves, oregano and chili sauce; simmer, covered, 30 minutes. Add olives and simmer 5 minutes.

Serves 6.

Per serving: 294 calories, 8.5g total fat (1g saturated), 44g carbohydrate, 13.7g protein, 9g fiber, 428mg sodium.

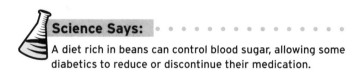

Science Says: • • • • • • • • • • • •
A diet rich in beans can control blood sugar, allowing some
diabetics to reduce or discontinue their medication.

Spinach-Mushroom Frittata Pie

1   **10-ounce package frozen chopped spinach, thawed and squeezed dry**

4   **eggs or 1 cup egg substitute**

1   **cup part-skim ricotta cheese**

3/4   **cup freshly grated Parmesan cheese**

3/4   **cup chopped mushrooms (white button, crimini or portobello)**

1/2   **cup finely chopped scallions with some green tops (about 4 large)**

1/4   **teaspoon dried Italian seasonings**

    Salt and freshly ground black pepper, to taste

WHY IT'S GOOD FOR YOU:

* Antioxidants in spinach and scallions

* High lutein and choline in egg yolks

* Plus: Mushrooms are anti-cancer

Preheat oven to 375°F. In a large bowl, whisk together all ingredients until well mixed. Spray a 9-inch pie plate with cooking spray and fill with the spinach-egg mixture. Bake for 30 minutes, or until browned and set. Let cool for 20 minutes, cut into wedges and serve.

Serves 6.

Per serving with eggs: 178 calories, 10g total fat (5g saturated), 6g carbohydrate, 15.5g protein, 1g fiber, 358mg sodium.

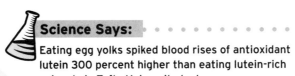

Science Says: Eating egg yolks spiked blood rises of antioxidant lutein 300 percent higher than eating lutein-rich spinach, in Tufts University tests.

Down-Home Vegetable Frittata

1   teaspoon extra-virgin olive oil

1   medium yellow onion, chopped

1   clove garlic, minced

1   green bell pepper, chopped

4   beaten eggs or 1 cup egg substitute

2   tablespoons freshly grated Parmesan cheese

1/2 teaspoon chopped fresh rosemary or oregano or 1/4 teaspoon dried

Salt and freshly ground black pepper, to taste

1   large baking potato, cooked and cubed

1   medium tomato, chopped

Spicy tomato salsa, for garnish

WHY IT'S GOOD FOR YOU:
* Antioxidants in onion, garlic, pepper, tomato, herbs
* Antioxidants and brain-protecting choline in eggs

Add olive oil to a large nonstick skillet; sauté onion, garlic and pepper until soft, about 3 minutes. Combine eggs, cheese, herbs, salt and pepper. Add potato and tomato to the skillet and immediately top with the egg mixture. Cook over low heat until nearly cooked through; top should be slightly uncooked. Transfer skillet under broiler for a minute or until top is done and slightly browned. Loosen frittata around the edge with a narrow spatula and slide frittata from skillet to a plate. Cut in quarters. Serve with spicy tomato salsa.

Serves 4.

Per serving with eggs: 209 calories, 7.3g total fat (2.3g saturated), 26g carbohydrate, 1g protein, 3g fiber, 130mg sodium.

Science Says: Eating about three eggs a week as a teenager cut odds of breast cancer risk later in life by 18 percent, find Harvard researchers.

Soy Sloppy Joes

1   **cup textured soy protein***

7/8 **cup boiling water**

1   **tablespoon extra-virgin olive oil**

1   **green bell pepper, cored and diced**

1   **cup chopped yellow onions**

1   **cup strained no-salt-added tomatoes (Pomi) or tomato sauce**

1   **cup chili sauce or barbecue sauce**

½   **teaspoon chili powder or more to taste**

    Salt and freshly ground black pepper, to taste

Add textured vegetable protein to boiling water; stir and let sit for 5 minutes or until needed. Heat olive oil a large skillet and sauté green pepper and onions until soft. Stir in tomatoes, chili or barbecue sauce, textured vegetable protein and chili powder. Simmer for 5 to 10 minutes or until heated through. Season with salt and pepper. Serve on whole-wheat buns or bread.

Serves 4.

*Textured soy protein, a flaky, dried soy product, is available in health food stores and some supermarkets. It is sometimes called textured vegetable protein (TVP).

Per serving: 217 calories, 5.3g total fat (0.5g saturated), 29g carbohydrate, 9.8g protein, 5g fiber, 923mg sodium.

Science Says: • • • • • • • • • • • • • • • • • • •
Two to four servings of soy-protein foods a week are a healthful substitute for animal protein, says Harvard nutritionist Walter Willett.

Pepper, Onion & Feta Pizza

3 cups chopped mixed bell peppers,
(red, green, yellow and/or orange)

1 cup sliced yellow or red onions,
separated into rings

3 cloves garlic, crushed

1½ teaspoons dried Italian herbs

Salt to taste

¼ teaspoon dried red pepper flakes, optional

2 tablespoons extra-virgin olive oil

¾ cup crumbled herbed feta cheese

1 12-inch thin pizza crust, homemade or prepared
(such as Boboli)

WHY IT'S GOOD FOR YOU:

＊Super antioxidants in peppers, onion, garlic and herbs

＊**Plus:** Vegetables help lower blood pressure

Preheat oven to 450°F. In a bowl, combine peppers, onions, garlic, seasonings and olive oil. Place crust on large pizza pan. Top with vegetable mixture. Sprinkle on cheese. Bake for 10-12 minutes. Cut into 6 slices.

Per slice: 258 calories, 11.6g total fat (4g saturated), 30g carbohydrate, 8g protein, 2g fiber, 488mg sodium.

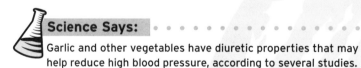

Science Says: Garlic and other vegetables have diuretic properties that may help reduce high blood pressure, according to several studies.

Pizza with Mushroom "Sausage"

Mushroom "Sausage"

 3 cups chopped portobello mushrooms

 2 tablespoons extra-virgin olive oil

 3 cloves garlic, crushed

 2 teaspoons fennel seed

 1½ teaspoons dried Italian herbs

 ¾ teaspoon dried red pepper flakes

 Salt and freshly ground black pepper, to taste

WHY IT'S GOOD FOR YOU:

✳ Antioxidants in garlic, herbs

✳ Anti-cancer chemicals in mushrooms

✳ Good fat in olive oil

Combine all ingredients and set aside 10-15 minutes to absorb flavors.

Pizza

 1 12-inch thin pizza crust, homemade or prepared (such as Boboli)

 1 8-ounce can no-salt-added tomato sauce

 1½ cups chopped green bell pepper

 1½ cups chopped red onion

 ¾ cup shredded part-skim mozzarella cheese

Preheat oven to 450°F. Place crust on large pizza pan. Top with sauce, mushroom "sausage" mixture, green peppers, onions and cheese. Bake for 10-12 minutes. Cut into 6 slices.

Per slice: 329 calories, 11.4g total fat (3.4g saturated), 45g carbohydrate, 14g protein, 4g fiber, 482mg sodium.

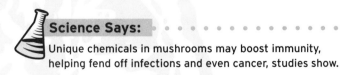

Science Says: · · · · · · · · · · · · · · · ·
Unique chemicals in mushrooms may boost immunity, helping fend off infections and even cancer, studies show.

· ·

Spaghetti with Roasted Red Peppers, Parsley and Walnuts

½ **pound spaghetti or fettuccine**

1 **7-ounce jar roasted red peppers, drained and coarsely chopped***

2 **cups chopped fresh parsley**

¾ **cup walnut pieces**

3 **tablespoons extra-virgin olive oil**

1 **clove garlic, crushed**

Salt and freshly ground pepper, to taste

*You can also substitute 1 cup chopped, juicy, ripe tomatoes.

In a large pot of boiling water, cook pasta until al dente. While pasta is cooking, toss together red peppers, parsley and walnuts. Combine cooked pasta with olive oil and garlic. Add pepper-parsley mixture, salt and pepper and toss again. Serve immediately, at room temperature or chilled.

Serves 6.

Per serving: 312 calories, 17g total fat (1.9g saturated), 35g carbohydrate, 7.4g protein, 3g fiber, 55mg sodium.

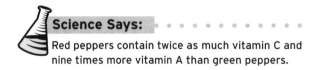

Science Says: Red peppers contain twice as much vitamin C and nine times more vitamin A than green peppers.

Ziti Spinach Alfredo

8   ounces ziti or penne pasta

1   medium onion, chopped

2   large cloves garlic, crushed

1   tablespoon extra-virgin olive oil

2   tablespoons butter

3   tablespoons all-purpose flour

2½ cups fat-free half-and-half

1   cup grated Parmesan cheese

2   teaspoons dried Italian seasoning

    Salt and freshly ground black pepper, to taste

1   14.5-ounce can diced tomatoes with Italian herbs

1   10-ounce package frozen chopped spinach, thawed and drained

> **WHY IT'S GOOD FOR YOU:**
> * Antioxidants in onion, garlic, tomatoes and spinach
> * Low calorie

In a large pot of boiling water, cook pasta until al dente. In a small saucepan, sauté onions and garlic in olive oil until soft. In a large saucepan, melt butter; add flour and stir. Slowly add half-and-half and simmer, stirring constantly, until thickened. Add cheese and seasonings; stir until cheese melts. Add tomatoes, spinach and onion mixture; heat through. Pour over warm pasta, toss and serve.

Serves 8.

Per serving: 281 calories, 8g total fat (4g saturated), 38g carbohydrate, 11g protein, 2g fiber, 436mg sodium.

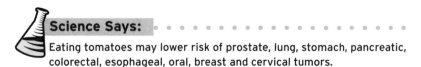

Science Says: Eating tomatoes may lower risk of prostate, lung, stomach, pancreatic, colorectal, esophageal, oral, breast and cervical tumors.

Fettuccine with Fresh Tomato-Basil Sauce

5 medium, ripe tomatoes (1½ pounds), diced

1 medium red onion, chopped

1 clove garlic, crushed

¾ cup shredded fresh basil

1 cup chopped fresh parsley

1/3 cup coarsely crumbled feta cheese

3 tablespoons extra-virgin olive oil

2 teaspoons balsamic vinegar

Salt and freshly ground black pepper, to taste

1 pound fettuccine

¼ cup chopped black olives, preferably oil-cured, optional

WHY IT'S GOOD FOR YOU:

* Antioxidants in tomatoes, onion, garlic, basil, parsley

* Good fat in olive oil

In a large bowl, combine tomatoes, onions, garlic, basil, parsley, cheese, oil, vinegar, salt and pepper. In a large pot of boiling water, cook fettuccine until al dente. Drain pasta and combine with tomato-basil mixture. Top with olives, if desired. Serve chilled or at room temperature.

Serves 8.

Per serving: 311 calories, 8.5g total fat (2.4g saturated), 49g carbohydrate, 10g protein, 3.2g fiber, 129mg sodium.

Science Says: · · · · · · · · · · · · · · ·

In studies of elderly Catholic nuns, those with the highest blood levels of lycopene (from eating tomatoes) had a lower risk of dementia.

· · · · · · · · · · · · · · · · · · · ·

Lasagna with Greens and Onions

 5 cloves garlic, crushed

 2 cups chopped yellow onions

 1 tablespoon extra-virgin olive oil

16 ounces frozen chopped kale, collard greens
    or spinach

 3 eggs or ¾ cup egg substitute

32 ounces fat-free cottage cheese

 1 teaspoon dried basil

 1 teaspoon dried oregano

 4 cups tomato pasta sauce, homemade or canned,
    low sodium, such as Classico Sweet Basil Marinara

 9 lasagna noodles, cooked*

 1 cup freshly grated Parmesan cheese

*Or use no-boil lasagna noodles.

Science Says: • • • • • •

A daily fare of kale (lutein), tomato
juice (lycopene) and sweet potatoes
(beta carotene) boosted ability
of immune responses to fight off
viruses, in USDA test subjects.

• • • • • • • • • • • • • •

Preheat oven to 350°F. Sauté garlic and onions in olive oil until soft, about 3 minutes. Cook greens as directed on package; cool. Squeeze out excess water with hands. If using whole eggs, whip lightly with a fork. In a bowl, combine eggs, cottage cheese, herbs, garlic, onions and greens. Spread a thin layer of pasta sauce on bottom of a 9-by-13-inch baking dish. Lay 3 noodles in baking dish; top with half the cheese-kale mixture, followed by 3 more noodles, the remaining cheese-kale mixture, finishing with the last 3 noodles. Pour sauce on top; sprinkle with Parmesan. Bake, uncovered, for 45 minutes.

Serves 8.

Per serving: 392 calories, 9.6g total fat (3g saturated), 47g carbohydrate, 29g protein, 4.5g fiber, 984mg sodium.

Pasta with Quick Onion-Pepper Sauce

2 tablespoons extra-virgin olive oil

4 large cloves garlic, thinly sliced

½ cup coarsely chopped walnuts

10 cherry tomatoes, halved

2 medium bell peppers (green, red and/or yellow), cored and cut lengthwise into ½-inch-long strips

1½ medium yellow onions, thinly sliced

1½ cups coarsely chopped fresh parsley

Freshly ground black pepper, to taste

3 cups cooked rotelle or other curly pasta (about 6 ounces dry)

WHY IT'S GOOD FOR YOU:

* Antioxidants in garlic, onion, tomatoes, peppers and parsley
* Good fats in olive oil and walnuts

Heat olive oil in large skillet over medium heat, add walnuts and garlic and sauté about 3 minutes. Add tomatoes; cook until soft, about 5 minutes. Put peppers and onions in large microwave-safe bowl; cover. Microwave on high until tender. Transfer peppers and onions to skillet and add parsley; stir to combine thoroughly. Put pasta in large shallow bowl and toss with onion-pepper sauce.

Serves 4.

Per serving: 367 calories, 17g total fat (1.9g saturated), 46g carbohydrate, 9.6g protein, 4.7g fiber, 19mg sodium.

Science Says:

Your body absorbs two and a half times more antioxidant lycopene from cooked tomatoes as from raw tomatoes. Adding oil also hypes absorption of lycopene.

Pasta with Vegetables and Garbanzos

2 tablespoons extra-virgin olive oil

2 large cloves garlic, crushed

4 ounces ground turkey breast

1 10-ounce package frozen spinach, thawed, drained and squeezed dry

1 8-ounce can garbanzo beans (chick peas), drained and rinsed

2 14.5-ounce cans diced no-salt-added tomatoes

½ cup feta cheese (about 3 ounces), cubed or crumbled

1½ teaspoons fennel seeds

1 teaspoon dried oregano

¼ teaspoon hot pepper flakes or to taste

Salt and freshly ground black pepper, to taste

8 ounces dry pasta, such as fettuccine or penne, cooked until al dente

WHY IT'S GOOD FOR YOU:
* Antioxidants in garlic, spinach and tomatoes
* Fiber in garbanzo beans
* **Plus:** Legumes keep down blood sugar spikes

In a large skillet, heat olive oil and sauté garlic 30 seconds. Add turkey and sauté until slightly browned, about 4 minutes. Add spinach, beans, tomatoes, cheese, fennel, oregano and pepper flakes and simmer covered until heated through, about 10 minutes. Season with salt and pepper. Serve over cooked pasta.

Serves 6.

Per serving: 307 calories, 9.5g total fat (2.9g saturated), 41g carbohydrate, 15.6g protein, 4.2g fiber, 264mg sodium.

Science Says: • • • • • • • • • • • • • • • • • •
Men who ate ten or more servings of tomatoes per week (raw tomatoes, tomato sauce, tomato juice and pizza) cut odds of prostate cancer by 35 percent, reported Harvard research.
• •

Pasta Salad with Beans and Smoked Salmon

8   ounces corkscrew pasta

4   ounces smoked salmon (nova, not lox), cut into julienne strips

1   16-ounce can garbanzo beans (chick peas), drained and rinsed (1½ cups)

½   cup minced red onion

3   tablespoons capers, drained and rinsed

3   tablespoons chopped black olives, preferably oil-cured

1   cup finely chopped fresh parsley

Dressing:

¼   cup extra-virgin olive oil

2   cloves garlic, minced

2   tablespoons fresh lemon juice

Freshly ground black pepper, to taste

Whisk together the dressing ingredients. In a large saucepan of boiling water, cook pasta until al dente, drain and put in a bowl. Add dressing and all other ingredients; toss. Serve at room temperature.

Serves 6.

Per serving: 320 calories, 13.5g total fat (1.8g saturated, 8.3g monounsaturated), 39g carbohydrate, 11.6g protein, 3.6g fiber, 498mg sodium.

Science Says: ·

Black olives contain more antioxidants than green olives.

· ·

Macaroni-Salmon Salad with Curry Dressing

1   8-ounce salmon fillet, skin removed
     (or 7.5 oz can red salmon)

1   cup dry pasta, such as macaroni or small shells

½ cup minced red or yellow onion

1   cup diced celery

1   medium-to-large apple, such as Gala, diced

½ cup chopped walnuts or dry-roasted unsalted peanuts

    Freshly ground black pepper, to taste

Curry Dressing:

1   6-ounce carton (¾ cup) fat-free plain yogurt

2   tablespoons extra-virgin olive oil

1   tablespoon curry powder

2   teaspoons fresh lemon juice

2   cloves garlic, crushed

1   teaspoon Dijon mustard

½ teaspoon salt or to taste

WHY IT'S GOOD FOR YOU:

* Good omega-3 fat in salmon
* Antioxidants in onion, celery and apples
* Good fat in nuts
* **Plus:** Curcumin in curry is anti-inflammatory and anti-cancer

Science Says:

Celery contains an aromatic chemical – 3-n-butyl phthalide – that lowered blood pressure in animals in doses comparable to eating four stalks of celery daily, reports University of Chicago research.

Poach or bake salmon, and cut into chunks. Cook pasta according to package directions; drain. In a large bowl, combine salmon and other salad ingredients. In small bowl, combine dressing ingredients. Pour dressing over salad and toss. Refrigerate or serve at room temperature.

Serves 8.

Per serving: 213 calories, 11g fat (1g saturated), 18g carbohydrate, 12g protein, 2g fiber, 208mg sodium.

Note: You can also use this curry dressing for fish or salads.
It is so good, you can eat it by the spoonful.

Spaghetti and Tofu in Spicy Peanut Sauce

4 cups cooked whole-grain thin spaghetti, drained and rinsed

1 cup carrots, cut into matchsticks

8 ounces firm tofu, cubed

1/3 cup thinly sliced green onions

1/4 cup chopped dry roast peanuts, unsalted

Peanut Sauce:

1/3 cup smooth peanut butter, preferably natural

1/3 cup fat-free, reduced-sodium chicken broth.

1 tablespoon reduced-sodium soy sauce

1 tablespoon grated fresh ginger

1 teaspoon hot red pepper flakes

1 clove garlic, minced

1 1/2 tablespoons orange marmalade

WHY IT'S GOOD FOR YOU:

* Antioxidants in carrots
* Anti-cholesterol agents in tofu
* Anticoagulant activity in ginger
* **Plus:** Peanut butter dampens blood sugar and appetite
* Whole grains discourage heart disease

In a large bowl, combine Peanut Sauce ingredients. Add spaghetti, carrots and tofu. Toss to coat with sauce. Sprinkle with green onions and peanuts.

Serves 6.

Per serving: 282 calories, 11g total fat (2g saturated), 35g carbohydrate, 15g protein, 5.9g fiber, 217mg sodium.

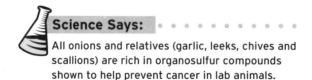

Science Says:

All onions and relatives (garlic, leeks, chives and scallions) are rich in organosulfur compounds shown to help prevent cancer in lab animals.

Picnic Rice Salad

4 cups cooked brown rice

1 2.5-ounce can sliced black olives, drained

6 scallions, thinly sliced, including 3 inches green

1 cup cooked green peas

2 large tomatoes, chopped (unpeeled)

¼ cup shredded basil leaves

⅓ cup shelled salted sunflower seeds

¼ cup extra-virgin olive oil

1½ tablespoons balsamic vinegar

Salt and freshly ground black pepper, to taste

In a large bowl, combine rice, olives, vegetables, basil and sunflower seeds. In a small bowl, whisk together oil, vinegar, salt and pepper. Add to rice mixture and toss.

Serves 6.

Per serving: 293 calories, 15g total fat (2g saturated), 35g carbohydrate, 6.3g protein, 5g fiber, 170mg sodium.

Science Says: In Harvard research, eating two-and-a-half servings of whole grains daily, such as brown rice, slashed women's risk of heart disease one-third to one-half.

Crunchy Tabbouleh

1   cup raw bulgur wheat, cooked and drained

3   large tomatoes, diced

1   large cucumber, peeled and diced

1   large green bell pepper, diced

4   spring onions, thinly sliced

¼   cup fresh mint leaves, shredded

⅓   cup fresh lemon juice

2   tablespoons extra-virgin olive oil

    Salt and freshly ground black pepper, to taste

Thoroughly combine all ingredients in a large bowl. Chill several hours before serving.

Serves 6.

Per serving: 102 calories, 3.5g total fat, (0.4g saturated), 17g carbohydrate, 2.6g protein, 5.3g fiber, 12mg sodium.

WHY IT'S GOOD FOR YOU:

*High fiber in bulgur wheat

*Antioxidants in tomatoes, cucumbers, peppers, onions and mint

*Low calorie and low sodium

*Plus: Whole grains help regulate insulin and blood sugar

Science Says:

Eating whole grains, such as bulgur wheat, cuts your risk of developing diabetes by 20 percent, finds University of Minnesota research.

Bulgur with Oranges

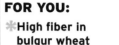

1	cup raw bulgur wheat, cooked and drained
1½	cups coarsely chopped cabbage
¾	cup sliced scallions with green
½	cup chopped walnuts
1	large orange, cut into chunks with ½ cup orange juice, or 1 11-ounce can undrained mandarin oranges
2	tablespoons distilled white vinegar
¼	teaspoon salt or to taste

WHY IT'S GOOD FOR YOU:
* High fiber in bulgur wheat
* Antioxidants in cabbage, onions, oranges
* Good fat in walnuts
* Low calorie and low saturated fat

Combine all ingredients in a large bowl. Chill several hours before serving.

Serves 6.

Per serving: 176 calories, 6.6g total fat (0.6g saturated), 27 g carbohydrate, 5g protein, 6.7g fiber, 105mg sodium.

Science Says: • • • • • • • • • • •
Eating bulgur and other whole grains can lower risk of colon and stomach cancer by as much as 50 percent, according to Italian researchers.

• • • • • • • • • • • • • • • • • • •

Grilled Salmon with Orange Glaze

½ cup orange marmalade

2 teaspoons sesame oil

2 teaspoons reduced-sodium soy sauce

½ teaspoon grated fresh ginger

1 clove garlic, crushed

3 tablespoons rice vinegar or other white vinegar

1 pound boneless, skinless salmon fillet,
   cut into four pieces

6 thinly sliced scallions with some green, optional

¼ cup toasted sesame seeds, optional

WHY IT'S GOOD FOR YOU:

* High omega-3 fat in salmon
* Antioxidants in orange rind, garlic, scallions
* Anticoagulant activity in ginger

Combine marmalade, oil, soy sauce, ginger, garlic and vinegar. Heat grill. Brush orange glaze on each side of salmon and grill about 5 minutes on each side. If desired, top with scallions and sesame seeds before serving.

Serves 4.

Per serving: 226 calories, 8g total fat (1.3g saturated), 15g carbohydrate, 23g protein, 0.2g fiber, 140mg sodium.

Science Says: ● ● ● ● ● ● ● ● ●

Eating fatty fish, such as salmon, could prevent an astounding 80 percent of sudden deaths from heart attacks, say Harvard investigators.

● ● ● ● ● ● ● ● ● ● ● ● ● ● ●

Chilled Salmon with Summer Tomato Salsa

4 4-ounce salmon fillets, skin removed

2 cups water

Tomato Salsa

1 cup chopped fresh tomato

½ Hass avocado, chopped

1 clove garlic, crushed

1 tablespoon balsamic vinegar

1 teaspoon extra-virgin olive oil

½ cup cooked corn kernels

¼ cup minced red onions

¼ cup chopped fresh cilantro, plus sprigs for garnish

Salt and freshly ground black pepper, to taste

1 lime, cut into wedges

Place salmon in a shallow microwave-safe bowl. Add water. Cover and microwave on high 7-9 minutes or until salmon is cooked as desired. Remove from water; refrigerate until cool.

In a small bowl combine all tomato salsa ingredients except lime. Refrigerate 30 minutes. Serve salmon surrounded by salsa and lime wedges. Garnish with cilantro sprigs.

Serves 4.

Per serving: 275 calories, 16g total fat (3g saturated), 10g carbohydrate, 22g protein, 2g fiber, 72mg sodium.

Science Says:

Women with the highest omega-3 fish oil in breast tissue were about 70 percent less apt to have breast cancer than women with the least omega-3.

Asian Fish with Vegetables

4   cups shredded savoy cabbage

1   medium red bell pepper, cut into slivers

6   scallions with green, sliced

2   4-ounce halibut or mahi-mahi fillets

Sauce:

2   large cloves garlic, crushed

1/3   cup dry-roasted unsalted peanuts, crushed in blender

2   tablespoons grated fresh ginger

1/3   cup water

1   teaspoon cornstarch

2   tablespoons reduced-sodium soy sauce

1   teaspoon sesame oil

1   tablespoon rice vinegar

1   tablespoon mirin (sweetened rice wine)

Garnish:

1/4   cup chopped fresh cilantro or parsley

1   lime

WHY IT'S GOOD FOR YOU:

✳ High omega-3 fat in halibut

✳ Antioxidants in cabbage, peppers and scallions

✳ Anti-clotting agents in ginger

✳ **Plus:** Cabbage has specific anti-cancer compounds

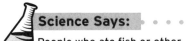

Science Says:

People who ate fish or other seafood at least once a week were 34 percent less apt to develop Alzheimer's disease or other forms of dementia, says a French study.

Spread vegetables over bottom of shallow microwave-safe dish. Top with fish. In a small bowl, combine sauce ingredients; pour over all. Cover tightly with microwave plastic wrap and microwave on high 8-10 minutes. Vegetables will be crisp-tender. Place each fillet on a plate; spoon vegetables and sauce around fish. Garnish with cilantro and a squeeze of lime juice. Serve with brown rice.

Serves 2.

Per serving (without rice): 375 calories, 15g total fat (2g saturated), 30g carbohydrate, 32g protein, 3.9g fiber, 726mg sodium.

Fiesta Seafood Casserole

 2 tablespoons extra-virgin olive oil

 4 large cloves garlic, crushed or minced

 1 medium onion, chopped

 1 medium green pepper, diced

 2 14.5-ounce cans diced no-salt-added tomatoes

 1 tablespoon chopped fresh thyme
     or 1 teaspoon dried thyme

16 ounces (2 cups) bottled clam juice or dry white wine

 2 cups instant brown rice

1½ cups diced smoked turkey

12 uncooked jumbo shrimp, shelled and deveined,
     tails on (about 12 ounces)

 8 ounces sea scallops, preferably dry-pack,
     each cut in half horizontally

 1 10-ounce package frozen peas

     Salt and freshly ground black pepper,
     to taste

12 mussels in shells

 2 canned roasted peppers, cut into strips
     about 5 inches long, 1 inch wide

WHY IT'S GOOD FOR YOU:

* Antioxidants in garlic, onions, peppers, tomatoes, peas and herbs

* High in low-fat, non-meat protein

* Shellfish lowers cholesterol

* **Plus:** Vegetables lower blood pressure and help prevent cancer

Science Says: · · · · ·

Eating a Mediterranean diet rich in seafood, fruits, vegetables, legumes, grains and olive oil, and low in meat, resulted in 72 percent fewer heart attacks and 60 percent fewer deaths among French heart patients than eating a standard-low fat diet.

· · · · · · · · · · · · ·

Preheat oven to 350°F. In a large skillet, heat olive oil; sauté garlic, onion and pepper until soft. Transfer to large shallow round or rectangular casserole. Stir in tomatoes, rice, turkey, scallops, shrimp, peas, salt and pepper. Top with mussels (push mussels down into mixture slightly with tops protruding) and strips of roasted pepper. Bake for 30 minutes.

Serves 7.

Per serving: 320 calories, 7.6g total fat (1.2g saturated), 39g carbohydrate, 27g protein, 4.2g fiber, 709mg sodium.

Tropical Mahi Mahi with Peanuts

1   pound mahi mahi, cut into 4 pieces*

1   banana, diced

1   8-ounce can crushed pineapple or tidbits, undrained

½   cup lite coconut milk

1   tablespoon peanut butter, preferably natural

   Dash hot pepper sauce

   Salt and freshly ground black pepper to taste

¼   cup flaked sweetened coconut

⅓   cup crushed unsalted peanuts

WHY IT'S GOOD FOR YOU:

* Peanuts suppress blood sugar rises and dampen appetite
* High potassium in bananas and pineapple
* Good protein and fat in fish
* Plus: Peanuts are rich in bone-protecting boron

Preheat oven to 350°F. Place fish in a small shallow microwave-safe dish or pie plate. Combine banana and pineapple. Microwave coconut milk 1 minute; stir in peanut butter, hot pepper sauce, salt and pepper. Add to fruit. Pour fruit mixture over fish. Top with flaked coconut. Bake 15 minutes. Put under broiler to brown top if necessary. Serve with peanuts and brown rice.

You can substitute other white fish, such as bass, tilapia or flounder.

Serves 4.

Per Serving: 291 calories, 12g total fat (3.5g saturated), 22g carbohydrate, 26g protein, 2g fiber, 123mg sodium.

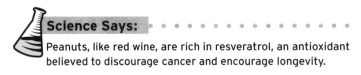

Science Says:

Peanuts, like red wine, are rich in resveratrol, an antioxidant believed to discourage cancer and encourage longevity.

Stir-Fry Scallops with Walnuts and Snow Peas

2 teaspoons sesame oil mixed with 2 teaspoons canola oil

3 cloves garlic, crushed

8 scallions, including some green,
  cut into 1"-2"-long diagonal slices

1½ cups snow peas

1 cup walnut halves, toasted*

1¼ pounds sea scallops, preferably dry pack,
  halved horizontally

Soy-Ginger Sauce:

1 tablespoon cornstarch

¼ cup fat-free, reduced sodium chicken
  or vegetable broth

2 tablespoons dry sherry

2 tablespoons reduced-sodium soy sauce

1 heaping teaspoon grated fresh ginger

¼ teaspoon hot pepper flakes or to taste

WHY IT'S GOOD FOR YOU:

* High protein in scallops
* Good fat in walnuts
* Antioxidants in snowpeas, garlic and scallions

Science Says:

Walnuts are a very high source of plant omega-3s, which the body can convert to long-chain omega-3s, the type found in fish.

To make the Soy-Ginger Sauce, combine cornstarch, broth, sherry, soy sauce, ginger and pepper flakes; set aside.

Heat 2 teaspoons of the oil in a wok or large skillet, over medium high heat. Add garlic, scallions and snow peas and stir-fry 3 minutes or until they are crisp tender. Remove to a serving bowl. Add remaining oil. When hot, stir-fry scallops 2 minutes. Stir in Soy-Ginger Sauce and cook until slightly thickened, about 2 minutes. Add scallions, snow peas, toasted walnuts. Cook about 1 minute – be careful to not overcook scallops. Serve at once with brown rice.

*Toast walnuts in 350°F oven 5 minutes.

Serves 6.

Per Serving: 258 calories, 14g total fat (1.3g saturated), 12g carbohydrate, 20g protein, 2.3g fiber, 430mg sodium.

Gingery Fish Kabobs with Pineapple

1 **tablespoon cornstarch**

2 **cups pineapple juice, preferably fresh**

2 **tablespoons reduced-sodium soy sauce**

1½ **tablespoons white vinegar**

2 **cloves garlic, crushed**

3 **tablespoons minced fresh ginger**

1¼ **pounds firm fish, such as salmon fillet, tuna steak or halibut, cut into chunks.***

4 **cups fresh pineapple cut into large chunks. (or substitute canned unsweetened pineapple chunks)**

1 **large onion, cut in wedges**

In a small saucepan, dissolve cornstarch in pineapple juice. Add soy sauce, vinegar, garlic and ginger and simmer until slightly thickened, about 7 minutes. Let cool. Combine fish, pineapple chunks and pineapple juice mixture in a shallow dish. Cover and marinate in the refrigerator for ½ hour. Thread fish, pineapple and onion onto skewers. Place skewers on a hot grill (or under a broiler) until fish has reached desired doneness. Serve with rice. If you like, bring the marinade to a boil and use as a sauce over fish and rice.

*For variety use more than one type fish.

Serves 6.

Per serving: 279 calories, 10.7g total fat (2g saturated), 25g carbohydrate, 20g protein, 1.3g fiber, 250mg sodium.

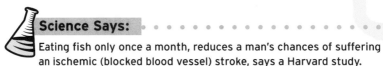

Science Says: Eating fish only once a month, reduces a man's chances of suffering an ischemic (blocked blood vessel) stroke, says a Harvard study.

Salmon and Mashed Potato Casserole

2 cups frozen mashed potatoes, made with fat-free milk

1 6-ounce can red or pink salmon, skin removed, flesh flaked

3/4 cup fresh or frozen corn kernels

2 ounces canned chopped green chiles, drained

2 scallions, chopped

Salt and freshly ground pepper, to taste

1/2 cup shredded low-fat sharp cheddar cheese

Preheat oven to 400°F. With a fork, gently combine mashed potatoes, salmon, corn, chiles and onions. Season with salt and pepper. Spray a pie pan with olive or canola oil. Spread potato mixture in pan. Sprinkle on cheese. Bake 15-20 minutes. If desired, put under broiler until top is slightly browned.

Serves 4.

Per serving: 224 calories, 3.2 g total fat (0.8 saturated), 30 g carbohydrate, 16 g protein, 3.5 g fiber, 501mg sodium.

Note: Don't eat salmon skin, which can contain concentrations of potentially toxic PCBs. Virtually all canned salmon is wild, not farmed.

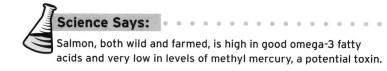

Science Says: Salmon, both wild and farmed, is high in good omega-3 fatty acids and very low in levels of methyl mercury, a potential toxin.

Elegant Shrimp Cassoulet

3   cloves garlic, peeled and sliced thin

1   cup chopped yellow onion

1   medium green bell pepper, chopped

1   tablespoon extra-virgin olive oil

2   19-ounce cans cannellini beans, drained and rinsed

1   14.5-ounce can diced tomatoes

1   cup fat-free, reduced-sodium chicken
    or vegetable broth

1/2   teaspoon each dried basil and thyme

1/2   cup kalamata olives, pitted and halved

3/4   pound large shrimp (raw or cooked), shelled, deveined and halved

1/2   cup dry bread crumbs

1/4   cup freshly grated Parmesan cheese
      Salt and freshly ground black pepper, to taste

Preheat oven to 400°F. In large pan, sauté garlic, onion and green pepper in oil over medium heat until soft, about 5 minutes. Add beans, tomatoes, broth, herbs, olives, salt and pepper. Bring to simmer. Add shrimp; cook 3 minutes. Turn into large baking dish. Top with bread crumbs mixed with Parmesan. Bake until bubbly, about 20 minutes. Brown top under broiler if desired.

Serves 8.

Per serving: 239 calories, 6.7g total fat (1.3g saturated), 26g carbohydrate, 18g protein, 6.5g fiber, 580mg sodium.

Science Says:

Men who eat the most garlic, onions and leeks — all members of the allium family — are much less apt to develop prostate cancer than non-allium eaters.

Tangy Fisherman's Stew

4   large cloves garlic, thinly sliced

1   small green bell pepper, diced

1   tablespoon extra-virgin olive oil

2   cups canned crushed tomatoes

2   cups water

2   medium potatoes (1 pound), peeled and cut into 2-inch chunks

1/2 teaspoon cumin, or to taste

1/3 cup chopped fresh parsley

1/4 teaspoon hot pepper flakes, or to taste

1   pound firm fish (such as tuna, snapper, grouper or sea bass), cut into 2-inch pieces

Salt and freshly ground black pepper, to taste

Sauté garlic and peppers in oil until tender. Add tomatoes, water, potatoes, cumin, parsley and hot pepper flakes; bring to a boil. Simmer 20 minutes, or until potatoes are tender. To slightly thicken stew, use the back of a spoon to mash some potatoes against the side of the pan. Add fish and simmer 10 minutes or until fish is done. Serve with warm Italian or French bread.

Serves 4.

Per serving: 297 calories, 9.4g total fat (2g saturated,) 23g carbohydrate, 30g protein, 3g fiber, 249mg sodium.

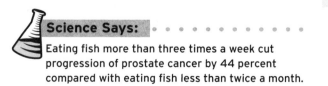

Science Says: Eating fish more than three times a week cut progression of prostate cancer by 44 percent compared with eating fish less than twice a month.

Microwave Salmon Teriyaki

3/4 pound salmon fillet

2 heaping tablespoons frozen orange juice concentrate

2 cloves garlic, crushed or minced

1 teaspoon finely minced fresh ginger

2 tablespoons reduced-sodium soy sauce

3 scallions, thinly sliced, including 3 inches of green

2 tablespoons toasted sesame seeds

WHY IT'S GOOD FOR YOU:

* Good omega-3 fat in salmon
* Antioxidants in orange juice and onions
* **Plus:** Ginger has anticoagulant, anti-inflammatory activity

Place salmon fillet, skin-side down, in a microwave-safe dish. Combine orange juice, garlic, ginger and soy sauce; pour over fish. Microwave, covered, on high for 7 minutes. Test for doneness; cook longer if needed. Serve on platter or plates, covered with sauce and sprinkled with scallions and sesame seeds.

Serves 2.

Per serving: 351 calories, 14.7g total fat (2.2g saturated), 16.6g carbohydrate, 37g protein, 1g fiber, 683mg sodium.

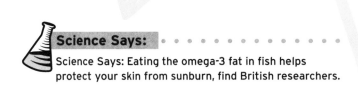

Science Says: • • • • • • • • • • • • • • • •
Science Says: Eating the omega-3 fat in fish helps protect your skin from sunburn, find British researchers.

• • • • • • • • • • • • • • • • • • •

Old-Fashioned Salmon Patties

1 large (14- or 15-ounce) can pink or red salmon*

8 low-fat or fat-free saltine crackers, crushed

2 beaten eggs (or ½ cup egg substitute)

Ground black pepper, to taste
(use cracked pepper for more bite)

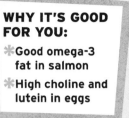

WHY IT'S GOOD FOR YOU:

* Good omega-3 fat in salmon
* High choline and lutein in eggs

Drain salmon; remove and discard skin. Mash salmon. Combine with crackers and eggs. Form into four patties; sprinkle with pepper. In a nonstick pan coated with canola oil, sauté over medium heat until patties are browned, 2-3 minutes per side.

Serve with lime or lemon wedges.

Or try this quick sauce: Combine ½ cup fat-free plain yogurt, 1 tablespoon prepared horseradish and a dash of lemon juice.

Pink and red salmon have equal amounts of beneficial omega-3 oils.

Serves 4.

SALMON: Per patty: 190 calories, 7.7g total fat (1.9g saturated), 5g carbohydrate, 24g protein, 0.2g fiber, 208mg sodium.

SAUCE: Per tablespoon: 9 calories, 0g total fat, 1g carbohydrate, 0.9g protein, 0g fiber, 13mg sodium.

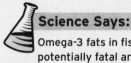

Science Says: • • • • • • • • • •
Omega-3 fats in fish act as a drug to suppress potentially fatal arrhythmias (irregular heart beats.)

• • • • • • • • • • • • • • • • • • •

Salmon with Scalloped Sweet Potatoes

3 medium sweet potatoes, peeled and thinly sliced (about 4 cups)

1 medium yellow onion, roughly chopped

1 teaspoon grated fresh ginger

1 cup orange juice

3 tablespoons orange marmalade

2 tablespoons melted trans-fat-free margarine or butter

Salt, to taste

1¼ pounds salmon fillet, skin removed, cut in 6 pieces

Freshly ground black pepper, to taste

¼ cup almond slivers, toasted

¼ cup Italian parsley sprigs

Preheat oven to 400°F. Combine sweet potatoes, onion, ginger, juice, 2 tablespoons of the marmalade, margarine and salt. Place in a 9 x 13- inch casserole dish, sprayed with cooking spray. Cover and bake 40 minutes. Remove from oven; top with salmon. Brush fish with the remaining 1 tablespoon marmalade; grind on pepper. Return to oven (uncovered) and bake 10 to 12 minutes, until fish is done to your liking. Garnish with almonds and parsley.

Serves 6.

Per serving: 340 calories, 14g total fat (2g saturated), 27g carbohydrate, 22g protein, 5g fiber, 90mg sodium.

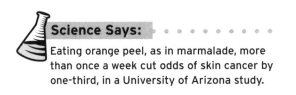

Science Says:

Eating orange peel, as in marmalade, more than once a week cut odds of skin cancer by one-third, in a University of Arizona study.

Pecan-Crusted Baked Salmon

1   tablespoon Dijon mustard

1   tablespoon fat-free plain yogurt
    or extra-virgin olive oil

3/4   pound salmon fillet or steak

1/4   cup ground pecans

    Freshly ground black pepper, to taste

Preheat oven to 450°F. Combine mustard and yogurt.
Spread mustard mixture on top of salmon, then
cover with pecans and pepper. Place on a baking
pan sprayed with olive oil or canola oil. Bake 12-15
minutes, or until fish flakes easily.

Serves 2.

Per serving: 404 calories, 26.2g total fat (4.2g saturated,
11.8 monounsaturated), 2g carbohydrate, 35g protein,
1g fiber, 368mg sodium.

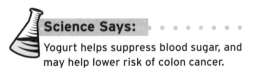

Science Says:
Yogurt helps suppress blood sugar, and
may help lower risk of colon cancer.

Pepper Salmon with Tropical Fruit Salsa

8   6-ounce salmon steaks

2   teaspoons cracked black pepper
    (do not substitute regular black pepper)

    Olive oil or canola spray

    Salt, to taste

Press ¼ teaspoon cracked pepper into each side of steaks and spray with olive oil. Grill 4-5 minutes on each side. Season with salt, if desired.

Serve each steak with ¼ cup Tropical Fruit Salsa.

Serves 8.

Per steak: 254 calories, 12g total fat (1.8g saturated), 7g carbohydrate, 33g protein, 0.3g fiber, 80mg sodium.

> **WHY IT'S GOOD FOR YOU:**
> *Good omega-3 fat in salmon
> *Antioxidants in pineapple, banana and onions

Science Says:

Omega-3 oils in fatty fish (salmon, tuna, sardines) may combat osteoarthritis by blunting inflammation and breakdown of cartilage, suggests a Welsh study.

Tropical Fruit Salsa

1   cup diced fresh pineapple

2   tablespoons fresh lemon juice

1   medium banana, diced

1   tablespoon apricot jam or orange marmalade

⅓   cup minced red onion

¼   teaspoon hot pepper flakes

2   tablespoons coconut flakes, optional

Combine ingredients in a small bowl.

Makes about 2 cups.

Per ¼ cup serving: 32 calories, 8g carbohydrate, 0.3g protein, 0.1g total fat, 6g fiber, 2mg sodium.

Honey Mustard Grilled Chicken

1 **boneless, skinless chicken breast, 8-10 ounces, cut in half**

2 **tablespoons honey**

2 **tablespoons Dijon mustard**

2 **cloves garlic, crushed**

1 **teaspoon fresh thyme**

Freshly ground black pepper, to taste

Microwave the chicken, covered, for 2½ minutes on high. Pat dry. Mix remaining ingredients and brush on both sides of chicken. Grill 5 minutes on each side or until done, brushing on more honey-mustard mixture if desired.

Serves 2.

Per serving: 222 calories, 2.4g total fat (0.5g saturated), 20g carbohydrate, 30.5g protein, 0.6g fiber, 280mg sodium.

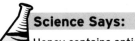

Science Says: • • • • • • • • •
Honey contains antioxidants and natural antibiotics to fight germs, including e coli. The darker the honey, the greater its potency.

15-Minute Chicken Chili

1	tablespoon canola oil or extra-virgin olive oil
10	ounces boneless, skinless chicken breast, cut into bite-size pieces
1½	tablespoons chili powder
1½	tablespoons ground cumin
2	14.5-ounce cans no-salt added diced tomatoes
1	15-ounce can no-salt added black, kidney or red beans
1	4.5 ounce can minced green chiles
1	cup yellow corn kernels, frozen or canned
	Salt and cayenne pepper, to taste

In a large saucepan, sauté chicken in oil over medium-high heat 3 minutes or until white. Stir in chili powder and cumin to coat chicken. Sauté 3-4 minutes. Add remaining ingredients; heat through.

Serves 4.

Per serving: 290 calories, 6g total fat (0.6g saturated), 36g carbohydrate, 26g protein, 9g fiber, 244 mg sodium.

Science Says:
Corn is a prime source of zeaxanthin, a strong antioxidant linked to lower rates of macular degeneration and cancer.

Company Garlic Chicken

2½ pounds boneless, skinless chicken breasts, cut into serving-size pieces

1 tablespoon canola oil

Salt and freshly ground black pepper, to taste

3 heads garlic, cloves separated but not peeled

1 tablespoon chopped fresh thyme or 1 teaspoon dried thyme leaves

1 tablespoon chopped fresh rosemary or 1 teaspoon dried rosemary

1½ cups dry white wine, or enough to cover chicken in casserole

¼ cup minced fresh parsley

WHY IT'S GOOD FOR YOU:

✳ High antioxidants in garlic, thyme and rosemary

✳ High protein, low fat in chicken breast

✳ Plus: Garlic fights cancer and heart disease

Preheat oven to 350°F. In a large skillet, fry chicken in oil over medium-high heat until golden brown. Salt and pepper chicken. Layer chicken in 4-quart casserole. Put garlic cloves on top of and among the chicken pieces. Sprinkle with thyme and rosemary. Add wine to cover. Cover and bake 1 hour, or until liquid is reduced and garlic is very soft. Before serving, sprinkle with parsley. Serve with toasted Italian or French bread (squeeze soft garlic onto bread).

Serves 6.

Per serving: 143 calories, 2.4g fat (0.4g saturated), 2.2g carbohydrate, 22.3g protein, 0.2g fiber, 153mg sodium.

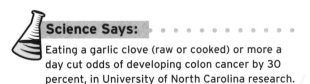

Science Says: Eating a garlic clove (raw or cooked) or more a day cut odds of developing colon cancer by 30 percent, in University of North Carolina research.

Chicken, Lentil and Vegetable Stew

2 pounds boneless, skinless chicken thighs or breasts, cut into chunks

1½ cups thick-sliced carrots

2 cups fresh spinach, sliced in ribbons

1 14.5 oz can diced tomatoes with juice

1 cup dry lentils

1 cup fat-free, reduced-sodium chicken broth

1 teaspoon dried Italian herbs

1 teaspoon crushed fennel seed

8 cloves garlic, peeled and cut in chunks

Salt and freshly ground black pepper, to taste

Parsley sprigs, for garnish

WHY IT'S GOOD FOR YOU:

*High antioxidants in carrots, spinach, tomatoes, garlic

*Low saturated fat

*Plus: Lentils have a low glycemic index, and suppress blood sugar rises.

*May help combat diabetes and heart disease

Place all ingredients in a large microwave-safe bowl. Stir to combine. Cover, microwave on high power about 25 minutes, or until chicken and vegetables are done. Add more broth if needed. Garnish with parsley.

Serves 6.

Per serving using chicken thighs: 330 calories, 6.7 g total fat (1.6 g saturated), 27g carbohydrate, 41g protein, 6 g fiber, 353 mg sodium.

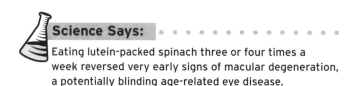

Science Says: • • • • • • • • • • • • • •
Eating lutein-packed spinach three or four times a week reversed very early signs of macular degeneration, a potentially blinding age-related eye disease.

• •

One-Dish Chicken Curry With Apples

1 tablespoon canola oil

Salt and freshly ground black pepper, to taste

2 pounds boneless, skinless chicken breast and thighs, cut into small serving pieces

3 medium Granny Smith apples, cored and chopped

2 large yellow onions, sliced thinly or chopped

6 large cloves garlic, minced or crushed

2 tablespoons curry powder, or more to taste

1½ teaspoons ground cumin

½ cup raisins

5 cups fat-free, reduced-sodium chicken broth

2 cups regular brown rice, uncooked (not instant)

WHY IT'S GOOD FOR YOU:

✳ Antioxidants in apples, onions, garlic, raisins

✳ Fiber in rice

✳ Low saturated fat

✳ Plus: Anti-inflammatory, anti-cancer curcumin in curry powder

✳ May help combat inflammation involved in arthritis and heart disease

In a large nonstick pot, heat canola oil. Salt and pepper the chicken, and brown it in oil. Remove chicken. Add apples, onions, garlic, curry and cumin. Sauté, stirring, 5 minutes. Add broth and raisins. Bring to a boil. Add rice and chicken. Cover, reduce heat and simmer until rice is tender, about 60 minutes.

Serve with condiments such as chutney, chopped peanuts, toasted coconut, chopped cilantro or sliced scallions.

Serves 8.

Per serving: 439 calories, 5.1g total fat (0.8g saturated), 62g carbohydrate, 37g protein, 5.4g fiber, 120mg sodium.

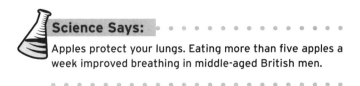

Science Says: • • • • • • • • • • • •

Apples protect your lungs. Eating more than five apples a week improved breathing in middle-aged British men.

Stir-Fry Chicken with Pineapple and Peppers

1   pound boneless, skinless chicken breast,
    cut into 1-inch pieces

2   tablespoons canola or sesame oil

6   large scallions, cut into 2-inch diagonal pieces
    with green

2   cups fresh or frozen bell pepper strips
    (red, green and/or yellow)*

1   20-ounce can chunk pineapple in juice

1/4 cup sliced almonds, optional

*Some frozen pepper packages contain onions,
 which is also okay to use.

Sauce:

1/4 cup reduced-sodium soy sauce

2   tablespoons white wine vinegar

2   tablespoons mirin (sweetened rice wine)

1   teaspoon grated fresh ginger

2   cloves garlic, crushed

1   tablespoon cornstarch

**WHY IT'S GOOD
FOR YOU:**

* Antioxidants in
  scallions, peppers
  and pineapple
* High protein,
  low fat in
  chicken breast
* Plus: Ginger
  fights inflam-
  mation and
  blood clots

Science Says:

Green peppers, pineapple,
tomatoes and carrots are tops
in certain phenolic acids, which
block formation of cancer-causing
nitrosamines in the body.

Combine sauce ingredients and stir to dissolve cornstarch. Set aside.

In a large skillet, stir-fry chicken in hot oil until browned, about 5 minutes: remove chicken from the pan and set aside. Add scallions, peppers
and pineapple to the pan; stir until heated through. Pour in sauce and
stir until thickened. Return chicken to skillet and heat through. Serve
with brown rice. If you like, top with almonds.

Serves 6.

Per serving: 222 calories, 5.6g total fat (0.9g saturated), 23g carbohydrate,
19g protein, 1.7g fiber, 454mg sodium.

Moroccan Chicken with Prunes

1	tablespoon canola oil
2	pounds boneless, skinless chicken breasts, cut into large chunks
1	cup fat-free, reduced-sodium chicken broth
1½	cups chopped onions
24	prunes (dried plums), preferably orange- or lemon-scented
1	cup prune juice
1	tablespoon ground cumin
2	teaspoons ground cinnamon
1	tablespoon reduced-sodium soy sauce
1½	tablespoons honey or brown sugar
⅓	cup whole raw unsalted almonds

WHY IT'S GOOD FOR YOU:
* Extremely high antioxidants in prunes and juice
* Antioxidants in onions
* Low saturated fat
* Magnesium in almonds
* **Plus:** Cinnamon helps suppress blood sugar

Preheat oven to 375°F. Heat oil in a skillet and brown chicken. Transfer chicken to a large casserole. In a separate bowl, combine broth, onions, prunes, prune juice, spices, soy sauce and honey or brown sugar. Cover and microwave on high 5 minutes. Pour over chicken. Stir in almonds. Cover and bake for 45 minutes. Serve with brown rice.

Serves 6.

Per serving: 387 calories, 9g total fat (1g saturated), 39g carbohydrate, 39g protein, 5.3g fiber, 370mg sodium.

Science Says:

Prunes contain a potent antioxidant — neochlorogenic acid — that can blunt artery damage from bad LDL cholesterol, finds University of California research.

Indian Chicken Stew with Coconut Milk

1   pound skinless, boneless chicken breast,
    cut into bite-size chunks

1   medium yellow onion, chopped or sliced

1   cup peeled potatoes cut into 1-inch chunks.

1   cup baby carrots, halved

1   9-ounce package frozen baby lima beans

1   14.5-ounce can diced tomatoes

1   cup canned coconut milk

1   cup fat-free, reduced-sodium chicken broth

1   tablespoon ground cumin

1   tablespoon curry powder

    Salt and freshly ground black pepper, to taste

¼   teaspoon hot sauce (such as Tabasco) or to taste

    Fresh parsley or cilantro, for garnish

WHY IT'S GOOD FOR YOU:

✳ Antioxidants in onion, carrots, beans, tomatoes

✳ High protein, low fat in chicken breast

✳ Plus: cumin and curry powder are antibiotic and anti-inflammatory, and cumin is anti-cancer

Put all ingredients in a large microwave safe bowl and mix thoroughly. Cover tightly and microwave on high for 30-40 minutes.

Serves 6

Per serving: 276 calories, 10g total fat (7g saturated), 25g carbohydrate, 24g protein, 5g fiber, 309 mg sodium.

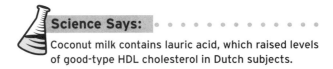

Science Says: • • • • • • • • • • • • • •
Coconut milk contains lauric acid, which raised levels of good-type HDL cholesterol in Dutch subjects.

• • • • • • • • • • • • • • • • • • • •

Quick Old-Fashioned Chicken Stew

2 teaspoons canola oil

¾ pound boneless, skinless chicken breast, cut into bite-size pieces

1 medium baking potato, peeled and cut into chunks

1 medium yellow onion, cut into eighths

1½ cups sliced carrots (or use baby carrots)

1 cup sliced celery

1 cup mixed frozen vegetables, such as green beans, corn, peas or cooked leftover vegetables

2 teaspoons crushed fresh rosemary or thyme, or to taste

1 12-ounce jar fat-free chicken gravy (such as Heinz)

Salt and freshly ground black pepper, to taste

WHY IT'S GOOD FOR YOU:

*Antioxidants in onion, carrots, celery, mixed vegetables.

*Low fat in chicken and gravy

Heat oil in a small skillet and brown chicken, about 5 minutes. Put potato, onion, carrots and celery into a large microwave-safe bowl; cover and microwave on high 12 minutes. Stir in chicken, chicken gravy, mixed vegetables, rosemary and freshly ground pepper to taste. Cover and microwave on high 10 minutes or until vegetables are done and mixture is heated through.

Serve with low-fat biscuits.

Serves 4.

Per serving: 255 calories, 3.8g total fat (0.5g saturated), 28g carbohydrate, 24.7g protein, 5.2g fiber, 617mg sodium.

Science Says:

Women who ate more canola oil and olive oil and less of other fats had about half the risk of breast cancer, finds a large Swedish study.

Mexican Bake

- **3** cups cooked rice, preferably brown
- **1** pound skinless, boned chicken breast cut into bite-size pieces, raw or cooked
- **2** 14.5 ounce cans no-salt-added tomatoes, diced or crushed
- **1** 15-ounce can black beans, drained and rinsed, or 1½ cups home-cooked unsalted beans.
- **1** cup frozen yellow corn kernels
- **1** cup chopped red bell pepper
- **1** cup chopped green poblano pepper or green bell pepper
- **1** tablespoon chili powder
- **1** tablespoon ground cumin
- **4** cloves garlic, crushed
- **1** cup shredded reduced-fat Monterey jack cheese
- **¼** cup jalapeño pepper slices, optional

Preheat oven to 400°F. Spread rice in a shallow three-quart casserole. Top with chicken. In a bowl, combine tomatoes, beans, corn, peppers, seasonings and garlic; pour over chicken. Top with cheese and optional jalapeños. Bake 45 minutes.

Serves 6.

Per serving: 378 calories, 6g total fat (2.9g saturated), 49g carbohydrate, 33g protein, 5.3g fiber, 236mg sodium.

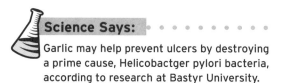

Science Says: Garlic may help prevent ulcers by destroying a prime cause, Helicobactger pylori bacteria, according to research at Bastyr University.

In-a-Hurry Chicken Curry

1½   tablespoons extra-virgin olive oil

1   boneless, skinless chicken breast (about ¾ pound), cut into bite-size pieces

1   medium yellow onion, chopped

1½   tablespoons curry powder

2   teaspoons cornstarch

1   cup fat-free, reduced-sodium chicken broth

¼   cup dried cherries or raisins

1   cup drained pineapple chunks

    Hot red pepper flakes, to taste, optional

WHY IT'S GOOD FOR YOU:
* Antioxidants in onions, cherries, pineapple
* High protein, low fat in chicken breast
* Plus: Curry powder helps protect aging brains

In a large skillet, heat olive oil over medium heat. Add chicken and onion; sauté 3 minutes. Add curry powder, stir to coat chicken and sauté 2 minutes. Blend cornstarch into chicken broth and add to chicken. Add cherries or raisins and heat until sauce bubbles. Add pineapple and optional pepper flakes. Simmer until pineapple is heated through and cherries or raisins are soft. Serve with brown rice.

Serves 4.

Per serving: 272 calories, 9g total fat (1.7g saturated), 19g carbohydrate, 29g protein, 2.5g fiber, 261mg sodium.

Science Says: • • • • • •
Curcumin, an antioxidant in curry powder, helped block development of cataracts in animals in University of Texas research.

Turkey Tortilla Pie

6   **corn tortillas**

1   **tablespoon canola oil**

1   **medium yellow onion, chopped**

1   **medium green bell pepper, diced**

2   **cloves garlic, crushed**

1   **pound ground turkey breast**

1   **tablespoon chili powder**

1   **teaspoon ground cumin**

2   **14.5-ounce cans no-salt added diced tomatoes**

1   **cup frozen corn kernels**

½   **cup chopped green or black olives**

1   **4.5 ounce-can chopped green chiles, drained**

1½   **cups reduced-fat shredded cheddar or pepper jack cheese**

WHY IT'S GOOD FOR YOU:

✳ Antioxidants in onions, garlic, bell pepper and chiles, tomatoes, corn and olives

✳ High protein, low fat in turkey breast

✳ Plus: Curry and chili powder are antibiotic and anti-inflammatory.

Science Says:

Eating lycopene-rich tomatoes discouraged thickening of artery walls that lead to blood clots in Finnish men.

Preheat oven to 400°F. Spray tortillas on both sides with butter-flavor oil spray. Cut into fourths. Spread on a baking sheet. Bake until crispy. (Do not turn off oven.)

In large skillet, heat oil. Add onion, green pepper, garlic and turkey. Sauté until turkey is done and vegetables are soft, about 10 minutes. Add tomatoes, corn, olives, spices and chopped chiles. Turn mixture into a shallow casserole dish. Crumble baked tortilla chips on top of pie. Sprinkle on cheese. Bake uncovered 20 minutes or until cheese melts.

Serves 6.

Per serving: 276 calories, 9.8g total fat (4g saturated), 16 g carbohydrate, 30g protein, 5g fiber, 638mg sodium.

Turkey Meatloaf with Caramelized Onion-Tomato Gravy

1½ pounds ground turkey breast

1 medium green bell pepper, finely chopped (1 cup)

1 medium yellow onion, chopped

½ cup bread crumbs

2 eggs, beaten, or ½ cup egg substitute

1 tablespoon Worcestershire sauce

3 cloves garlic, crushed

⅔ cup chili sauce or ketchup (reserve 2 tablespoons)

Salt and freshly ground black pepper, to taste

¼ cup freshly grated Parmesan cheese

Caramelized Onion-Tomato Gravy

1½ teaspoons extra-virgin olive oil

1 large onion, thinly sliced

1 cup stewed-type tomatoes

¾ cup fat-free half-and-half

1 tablespoon flour

Salt and freshly ground black pepper, to taste

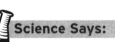

Science Says: • • • • • • • •

Onions and garlic contain 30 different anti-cancer agents and are consistently linked to lower rates of various cancers.

• • • • • • • • • • • • • • • • •

For meatloaf: Preheat oven to 350°F. Combine all ingredients except the cheese in a bowl. Form the mixture into one large loaf or two small loaves. Put in a shallow baking dish. Sprinkle reserved chili sauce and cheese on top. Cover and bake 30 minutes. Remove cover and bake 30 minutes more. Serve with gravy.

For Gravy: In a large skillet, heat olive oil; sauté onions until golden or caramelized, stirring frequently, 20-25 minutes. In a blender put tomatoes, half-and-half and flour; pulse twice. Add tomato mixture to onions; stir over medium heat until slightly thickened, about 10 minutes.

Serves 6.

Meatloaf per serving: 253 calories, 4g total fat, (1.3g saturated), 18.6g carbohydrates, 33g protein, 1g fiber, 652mg sodium.

Gravy per serving: 60 calories, 1.2g fat (0.1g saturated),10g carbohydrate, 0.9g protein, .9g fiber, 125mg sodium.

Turkey Marzetti

1 tablespoon canola oil

1 medium onion, chopped

1 medium green bell pepper diced

1 pound ground turkey breast

1 26-ounce carton strained tomatoes, no-sodium-added (such as Pomi) or 2 14.5-ounce cans no-salt-added diced tomatoes

1 10-ounce-can diced tomatoes and green chiles (such as Ro-Tel)

1 4.5-ounce can chopped green chiles

8 ounces dry noodles, cooked

1 cup shredded reduced-fat cheddar cheese

Salt and freshly ground black pepper, to taste

WHY IT'S GOOD FOR YOU:

*Antioxidants in onions, peppers, tomatoes and chiles

*High protein, low fat in turkey breast

Preheat oven to 400°F. In a large skillet, heat oil. Sauté onion, pepper and turkey 10-15 minutes. Add tomatoes and chiles; simmer 5 minutes. Spread cooked noodles over the bottom of a large shallow casserole; pour on turkey-tomato mixture and stir to combine. Sprinkle cheese over top and bake for 20 minutes. Put under broiler for a few minutes to brown top, if desired.

Serves 10.

Per serving: 233 calories, 4.2g total fat (1.6g saturated), 29g carbohydrate, 20g protein, 3.4g fiber, 288mg sodium.

Science Says: Veggies are bone-boosters. Eating onions, tomatoes, cucumbers, arugula, garlic, parsley and dill increased bone mass in animal studies.

Herbed Turkey Meatballs

1   pound ground turkey breast

½   cup freshly grated Parmesan cheese

2   tablespoons fennel seeds

2   tablespoons olive oil

1   cup whole-wheat bread crumbs

Combine all ingredients and form into small balls. Brown in a nonstick skillet. Use as you would beef, pork or other meat-balls – for example, in tomato sauce over pasta. Be sure turkey meatballs are cooked well-done, with no pink.

Serves 4.

Per serving: 272 calories, 11.4g total fat (3g saturated), 7.6g carbohydrate, 33.7g protein, 2g fiber, 310mg sodium.

Science Says:

Substituting poultry for red meat lowers risk of colon, breast and pancreatic cancer.

Greek-Style Turkey Burgers

1	pound ground turkey breast
⅓	cup chopped fresh mint
3	scallions including 3 inches green, finely minced
⅓	cup freshly grated Parmesan cheese
2	cloves garlic, crushed

WHY IT'S GOOD FOR YOU:

* High protein, low fat turkey
* Antioxidants in mint, scallions and garlic
* Low calorie and low fat

Combine all. Form into 4 patties. Grill until no pink remains. Serve on whole-wheat buns with Yogurt Sauce.

Yogurt Sauce: Mix 1 cup fat-free plain yogurt with ½ cup of a mixture of: chopped mint, chopped tomato, and chopped peeled and seeded cucumber. Add salt to taste.

Serves 4.

Per patty: 171 calories, 3g total fat (1.8g saturated), 2g carbohydrate, 32g protein, 1g fiber, 209mg sodium.

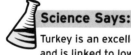

Science Says:
Turkey is an excellent source of B vitamins, zinc and selenium, and is linked to lower risk of heart disease and cancer.

Portobello Mushroom Burgers

⅓ cup minced onion

1 large clove garlic, crushed

1 tablespoon canola oil

6 ounces (3½ to 4 cups) diced portobello mushrooms

½ cup bread crumbs

1 beaten egg or ¼ cup egg substitute

Salt and freshly ground black pepper, to taste

WHY IT'S GOOD FOR YOU:

＊Antioxidants in onions, garlic and eggs

＊Plus: Portobello mushrooms are anti-cancer

In a large skillet over medium heat, sauté onion and garlic in oil for 2 minutes. Add mushrooms and cook, stirring frequently, until mushrooms are cooked down and liquid has disappeared, about 15-20 minutes. Let cool. Combine with rest of ingredients; form into 2 patties. Sprinkle on black pepper. Grill on both sides until heated through. Serve on whole-wheat buns.

Serves 2.

Per patty: 239 calories, 10.5g total fat (1.6g saturated), 27g carbohydrate, 9.6g protein, 3g fiber, 270mg sodium.

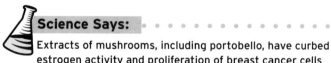

Science Says: · · · · · · · · · · · · · · · · ·
Extracts of mushrooms, including portobello, have curbed estrogen activity and proliferation of breast cancer cells in tests at the Beckman Research Institute in California.

· ·

Spinach-Stuffed Turkey Burgers with Blue Cheese

1   **pound ground turkey breast**

1   **10-ounce package frozen chopped spinach, thawed and squeezed dry**

2   **cloves garlic, crushed**

¼   **teaspoon hot red pepper flakes**

     Salt and freshly ground black pepper, to taste

Combine turkey, spinach, garlic and pepper flakes. Form 4 patties. Sprinkle with salt and pepper. Grill until done (no pink), 4-5 minutes each side. Serve on whole-wheat buns with Blue Cheese Sauce and onion and tomato slices.

Blue Cheese Sauce: Mix 2 tablespoons blue cheese with ½ cup fat-free sour cream.

Serves 4.

Per patty: 190 calories, 1.7g total fat (0.8g saturated), 9g carbohydrate, 33g protein, 2g fiber, 173mg sodium.

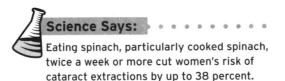

Science Says:

Eating spinach, particularly cooked spinach, twice a week or more cut women's risk of cataract extractions by up to 38 percent.

"Crab" Burgers

½ pound imitation crab
   (substitute real crab if desired)

½ cup fine bread crumbs

2 tablespoons finely chopped green bell pepper

1 teaspoon crab seasoning, such as Old Bay

½ cup egg substitute or 2 eggs

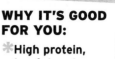

**WHY IT'S GOOD
FOR YOU:**
✳ High protein,
   low fat and
   low calorie
✳ Antioxidants
   and choline
   in eggs

Chop imitation crab coarsely. Combine all ingredients. Form into 4 patties. Spray both sides with olive or canola oil and grill 4 minutes each side. Serve on whole-wheat buns with dill pickles, lettuce or cabbage and one of the following sauces.

Tartar Sauce: Mix 2 tablespoons low-fat mayonnaise and 1 tablespoon pickle relish.

Cocktail Sauce: Mix 3 tablespoons ketchup, 1 teaspoon prepared horseradish and 1 teaspoon fresh lemon juice.

Serves 4.

Per patty: 116 calories, 2.2g total fat (0.2g saturated), 16g carbohydrate, 10.7g protein, 0.6g fiber, 818mg sodium.

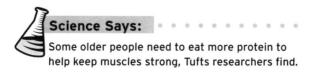

Science Says: • • • • • • • • • •
Some older people need to eat more protein to help keep muscles strong, Tufts researchers find.
• • • • • • • • • • • • • • • •

Gingered Tuna Burgers

1	**pound fresh tuna, finely chopped in food processor**
2	**large cloves garlic, crushed**
1½	**tablespoons reduced-sodium soy sauce**
2	**tablespoons grated fresh ginger**

Combine ingredients and form into 4 burgers. Grill or fry in a heavy, nonstick, sizzling-hot skillet to desired doneness – about 1 minute on each side for rare, 4 to 5 minutes for well done. Serve on whole-wheat buns topped with yogurt-cucumber sauce and pickled ginger slices.

Yogurt-Cucumber Sauce: Combine 1 cup fat-free plain yogurt with ⅓ cup peeled, chopped and seeded cucumber. Add salt to taste

Serves 4.

Per patty: 172 calories, 5.6g total fat (1.4g saturated), 2g carbohydrate, 27g protein, 1g fiber, 270mg sodium.

Science Says: Eating fish oil lowered signs of inflammation in the blood or C-reactive protein (CRP), which is associated with a higher risk of heart disease, reports University of North Carolina research.

Asian Salmon Burgers with Dilled Yogurt Sauce

1	14.5-ounce can pink or red salmon, skin removed
1	medium potato, baked or boiled, peeled
1	tablespoon reduced-sodium soy sauce
1½	teaspoons grated fresh ginger
2	cloves garlic, crushed
½	teaspoon cracked black pepper

Mash salmon and potato; mix in soy sauce, ginger and garlic. Form into 4 patties. Sprinkle with cracked black pepper on one side. Spray with olive or canola oil and grill on each side about 4 minutes. Serve on whole-wheat buns with dilled yogurt sauce and shredded raw cabbage.

Dilled Yogurt Sauce: Mix 1 cup fat-free plain yogurt with ⅓ cup chopped fresh dill. Add salt to taste.

Serves 4.

Per patty: 165 calories, 4.7g total fat (1.3g saturated), 10g carbohydrate, 20g protein, 0.7g fiber, 570mg sodium.

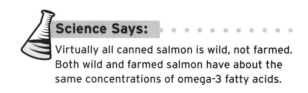

Science Says: Virtually all canned salmon is wild, not farmed. Both wild and farmed salmon have about the same concentrations of omega-3 fatty acids.

Blueberry Burgers

Don't be put off by the odd combination. The blueberries are virtually tasteless, but add moisture and help neutralize the threat of carcinogens that arise when the burger is grilled.

1	pound ground turkey breast or lean beef
1	cup blueberries or pitted tart cherries, ground in a food processor
3/4	teaspoon dried thyme
2	cloves garlic, crushed
	Salt and freshly ground pepper, to taste

WHY IT'S GOOD FOR YOU:
* Low fat, high protein in turkey
* Antioxidants in blueberries, garlic and thyme

Combine all ingredients. Form into 4 burgers. Grill well-done.

Serves 4.

Per patty: 149 calories, 0.9g total fat (0.2g saturated), 6g carbohydrate, 28g protein, 1g fiber, 58mg sodium.

Science Says:
Eating blueberries reverses some of the deleterious effects of aging in the brains of old rats and may even help overcome a genetic disposition toward Alzheimer's disease, says James Joseph of Tufts University.

Anti-Cancer Traditional Beef Burgers

From Dr. John Weisburger, as adapted from Jean Carper's book, *Stop Aging Now!*

1   **pound lean ground beef**

½   **cup textured vegetable protein
(a soy protein sold in health food stores
and some supermarkets)**

2   **tablespoons cold water
Salt and freshly ground black pepper, to taste**

Put all in a large bowl. Knead until combined. Form
into 4 patties. Grill, broil or fry. Serve on whole-grain
buns with sliced onion for antioxidant protection.

Serves 4.

Per patty: 241 calories, 14.9g total fat (5.9g saturated),
3g carbohydrate, 24g protein, 2g fiber, 63mg sodium.

**WHY IT'S GOOD
FOR YOU:**

✳ Mixing soy with
meat can reduce
by 90 percent
the production
of carcinogens
formed when
the meat cooks.

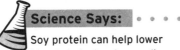

Science Says: • • • •

Soy protein can help lower
blood cholesterol according
to several studies and the
Food and Drug Administration.

• • • • • • • • • • • •

Anti-Cancer Marinades for Grilled Meats, Poultry and Fish

Marinating raw meat, poultry or fish in a thin sauce before grilling can dramatically reduce the amounts of carcinogens (HCAs) formed when the meat cooks. Here are three sauces that have been tested and proved to remove from 50 to 67 percent of the carcinogens formed during cooking.

Teriyaki Sauce

- 1 clove garlic, crushed
- 1 piece fresh ginger, minced
- 2 teaspoons brown sugar
- ½ cup reduced-sodium soy sauce
- ½ cup water

Combine ingredients. Pour over steaks, chicken or ribs. Cover and marinate overnight (12 to 16 hours) in the refrigerator. Makes 1 cup.

Turmeric-Garlic Marinade

- 2 teaspoons garlic powder
- 1 teaspoon ground turmeric
- ½ cup water or orange juice

Combine ingredients. Pour over steaks, chicken or ribs. Cover and marinate in the refrigerator for several hours.

Makes ½ cup.

Rosemary Tea Marinade

- 1 teaspoon crushed rosemary
- 1 clove garlic, crushed
- 2 teaspoons honey
- 2 teaspoons reduced-sodium soy sauce
- ½ cup concentrated tea (2 bags black tea brewed in ½ cup hot water for 5 minutes)

Add rosemary, garlic, honey and soy sauce to hot tea. Cool slightly. Pour over chicken, steaks, ribs, burgers or fish and marinate for at least 10 minutes.

Makes ½ cup.

Peach Crisp

1   **16-ounce bag frozen peach slices, thawed**

2   **tablespoons brown sugar**

½   **teaspoon ground cinnamon**

½   **cup no-added-fat granola**

    Fat-free vanilla ice cream or frozen yogurt, optional

Put fruit in a shallow microwave-safe dish. Toss fruit with sugar and cinnamon. Top with granola. Microwave 4 minutes on high or until fruit is warm. Top with optional ice cream.

Serves 4.

Per serving: 138 calories, 2.6g total fat (1.6g saturated), 29g carbohydrate, 2g protein, 3.4g fiber, 31mg sodium.

WHY IT'S GOOD FOR YOU:

* High antioxi- dants in peaches

* Very low fat

* Cinnamon helps suppress blood sugar rises

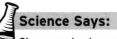

Science Says:

Cinnamon is also an antibiotic. In one test at Kansas State University, one teaspoon of cinnamon wiped out 99.5 percent of a million e coli bacteria.

Three-Berry Trifle

1   13.6-ounce Entenmann's fat-free loaf cake
    or other fat-free yellow cake

2   8-oz containers fat-free vanilla yogurt

1   15-ounce carton part-skim ricotta cheese

½   cup confectioners' sugar

2   cups fresh blueberries

4   cups fresh strawberries, hulled and sliced

½   cup dry sherry or almond-flavored liqueur such as Amaretto

½   cup slivered almonds, toasted

1   12-ounce bag frozen raspberries or 2 cups fresh raspberries,
    pureed and sweetened to taste.

Cut cake into 10 slices. Stir together yogurt, ricotta and confectioners' sugar. Reserve a dozen each of blueberries and strawberry slices for garnish. Combine remaining blueberries and strawberries.

To assemble trifle, place 4 cake slices in bottom of a clear glass bowl. Drizzle on one-third of the sherry or liqueur. Sprinkle one-third of the blueberry-strawberry mixture over cake. Spoon one-third of the yogurt mixture over berries. Make two more layers with remaining cake slices, sherry, berries and yogurt. Sprinkle almonds over top and decorate with reserved berries. Refrigerate for at least 3 hours.

To serve, spoon into dessert bowls and top with raspberry puree.

Serves 12.

Per serving: 279 calories, 6.3g total fat (2g saturated), 46g carbohydrate, 9.2g protein, 2g fiber, 222mg sodium.

Science Says: •
Blueberries and strawberries are antioxidant-rich and prevent and reverse brain aging in animals, according to Tufts University researchers.

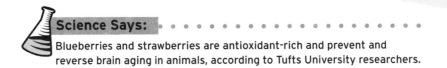

Maple Apple Crunch

4   **cooking apples, such as Granny Smith or McIntosh (about 1½ pounds), unpeeled and thinly sliced**

2   **tablespoons fresh lemon juice**

1   **teaspoon ground cinnamon**

½   **cup raisins**

¼   **cup maple syrup**

     Fat-free vanilla frozen yogurt, optional

Topping:

1   **cup regular rolled oats, uncooked**

⅓   **cup flour**

½   **cup sliced almonds**

2   **tablespoons canola oil**

2   **tablespoons maple syrup**

1   **teaspoon pure almond or vanilla extract**

WHY IT'S GOOD FOR YOU:

* High antioxidants in apples and raisins
* Oats fight cholesterol and high blood sugar
* Cinnamon helps suppress blood sugar rises

Preheat oven to 350°F. In a bowl, combine apple slices, lemon juice, cinnamon, raisins and syrup. In another bowl, combine topping ingredients. Spray a 9-by-13-inch baking dish with canola or olive oil cooking spray. Add apples, cover with foil and bake till apples are softened, about 30-40 minutes. Sprinkle with topping. Bake uncovered another 20-30 minutes until crisp. Serve warm with fat-free vanilla frozen yogurt if desired.

Serves 8.

Per serving: 236 calories, 7.5g total fat (0.7g saturated), 41g carbohydrate, 3.8g protein, 3.6g fiber, 4mg sodium.

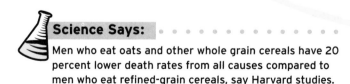

Science Says: Men who eat oats and other whole grain cereals have 20 percent lower death rates from all causes compared to men who eat refined-grain cereals, say Harvard studies.

Chocolate Cake with Raspberry Sauce

If you are surprised at using beans in a cake, be assured they make a very rich, moist chocolate cake. This cake is excellent for those who cannot eat wheat flour.

1½ cups semisweet chocolate chips

2   cups (19-ounce can) garbanzo beans (chick peas), drained and rinsed

4   eggs or 1 cup egg substitute

1   cup no-calorie sugar substitute (Splenda) or sugar

½   teaspoon baking powder

1   tablespoon confectioners' sugar

Quick Microwave Raspberry Sauce

½   cup seedless raspberry jam

2   teaspoons fresh lemon juice

1   pint fresh raspberries

WHY IT'S GOOD FOR YOU:
- Antioxidants in chocolate and raspberries
- Sugar-free, flour-free
- High fiber, protein in garbanzo beans (chick peas)
- Plus: garbanzos help counter blood sugar spikes

Science Says:

Eating legumes, including chick peas, once a week reduced risk of fatal pancreatic cancer by 40 percent, in Loma Linda University research.

Cake: Preheat oven to 350°F. In a small bowl, melt chocolate in microwave, 2 to 3 minutes. In a blender or food processor, combine beans and eggs; process until smooth. Stir in Splenda or sugar, baking powder, melted chocolate; process again until smooth.

Spray 8 4-ounce or 6-ounce oven-proof custard cups or ramekins with cooking spray. Divide batter evenly among baking dishes.

Bake for 25 minutes or until a knife inserted comes out clean. Cool. Place cakes upside down on a large plate, and sprinkle with confectioners' sugar. Serve on individual dessert plates with raspberry sauce, if desired.

Sauce: In a bowl, microwave jam until melted, 1 minute. Stir in juice and berries.

Serves 8.

Per cake: 238 calories, 13g fat (6g saturated), 28g carbohydrates, 3.7g fiber, 6.8 g protein, 140 mg sodium.

Sauce per serving: 64 calories, 0g fat, 17g carbohydrates, 1.7g fiber, .4g protein, 8mg sodium.

Blueberry Lemon Parfait

2   **cups fresh or thawed frozen blueberries**

2   **8-ounce containers fat-free lemon yogurt**

10   **gingersnaps, crumbled**

> In each of four parfait glasses or tall wine glasses, put ½ cup blueberries, followed by ½ cup yogurt, then the crumbled gingersnaps. Serve.
>
> Serves 4.
>
> **Per serving:** 147 calories, 2.9g total fat (0g saturated), 15g carbohydrate, 3.7g protein, 2g fiber, 160mg sodium.

WHY IT'S GOOD FOR YOU:

* Low saturated fat
* High antioxidants in blueberries
* Gut-protecting bacteria in yogurt
* Plus: Ginger is a mild anti-blood-clotting agent

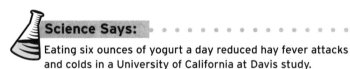

Science Says:

Eating six ounces of yogurt a day reduced hay fever attacks and colds in a University of California at Davis study.

10-Minute Berry Burritos à la Mode

2 **12-ounce bags frozen mixed berries (strawberries, blackberries, raspberries, blueberries)**

2 **tablespoons cornstarch (reserve 1 teaspoon)**

¼ **cup no-calorie sweetener such as Splenda or white sugar**

¼ **teaspoon ground cinnamon**

2 **flour tortillas (10-inch diameter)**
Butter-flavor cooking spray

3 **cups fat-free vanilla ice cream**

WHY IT'S GOOD FOR YOU:
✳ A super jolt of antioxidants in the berries
✳ Very low fat

Thaw and drain mixed berries: do not discard juice. Pour 1½ cups berry juice into a microwave-safe bowl. Add I cup of the berries. Set aside to use for the sauce. Preheat oven to 425°F.

Combine the remaining berries, 1 tablespoon plus 2 teaspoons cornstarch, Splenda or sugar, and cinnamon. Spray bottom of pizza pan or cookie sheet with butter flavor spray. Spread tortillas open on pan. Place equal amounts of berry mixture down the middle of each tortilla. Roll up like a burrito; place burrito seam-side down; spray top of burrito.

Bake 10 minutes or until slightly browned. Let cool for 10 minutes.

To make the sauce, stir 1 teaspoon cornstarch into berry/juice mixture. Microwave on high for 40 seconds or until thickened.

Cut each tortilla in three pieces. Serve each piece on a dessert plate with ½ cup ice cream. Top with warm sauce.

Serves 6.

Per serving: 231 calories, 2g total fat (0.2g saturated), 49g carbohydrate, 3.6g protein, 2.2g fiber, 138mg sodium.

Science Says: • • • • • • •
Among all fresh fruits, blueberries, blackberries, cranberries, strawberries and raspberries rank highest in antioxidant activity, in that order.

Dark Cherry Galette

1   refrigerator pie crust

2   12-ounce bags frozen dark sweet cherries*

1   tablespoon cornstarch

1   teaspoon pure almond extract

Preheat oven to 400°F. In a small saucepan, combine cherries, cornstarch and almond extract. Bring to a boil and simmer until thickened, about 2 minutes. Let cool 10 minutes. Roll pie crust to a 12-inch diameter; place on a pizza pan. Spread cherries in middle of crust; fold edges of crust up over cherries, to cover them partially. Bake 30 minutes or until crust is golden.

If you have too much fruit, save it as a topping.

Serves 6.

Per serving: 242 calories, 10g total fat (4g saturated), 37g carbohydrate, 1.4g protein, 1.7g fiber, 128mg sodium.

You can substitute peaches, blueberries or mixed berries.

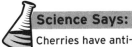

Science Says: • • • • • • • • • • • •
Cherries have anti-inflammatory activity. In one study, eating 10 ounces of sweet cherries cut blood urate levels – a sign of gout – about 15 percent in a group of women.

Chocolate Angel Bites

1   **cup finely ground walnuts**

½   **cup unsweetened cocoa powder**

1   **cup sugar**

3   **tablespoons canola oil**

8   **egg whites beaten until stiff with ½ teaspoon salt**

¼   **cup confectioners' sugar**

Preheat oven to 350°F. Combine nuts, cocoa, sugar, oil. Fold in ¼ of beaten egg whites. Add rest of egg whites. Spoon batter into nonstick or oiled mini-muffin pans. Bake for 12 minutes. Cool 5 minutes. Remove from pan and sprinkle with confectioners' sugar.

Makes 4 dozen.

Per mini-cake: 31 calories, 1g total fat (0.1g saturated), 5g carbohydrate, 0.8g protein, 0.3g fiber, 33mg sodium.

WHY IT'S GOOD FOR YOU:
* Very low saturated fat and cholesterol
* Antioxidants, trace minerals and omega-3 fat in walnuts
* Antioxidants in cocoa powder
* Nutrient-packed nuts replace flour

Science Says:

Eating three ounces of dark chocolate daily for two weeks lowered blood pressure in German subjects, about the same as going on a low-salt diet, said researchers.

Spicy Walnut Cookies

2   **cups walnut pieces**

⅓   **cup granulated white sugar**

1   **tablespoon ground cinnamon**

2   **egg whites, whisked until frothy**

Preheat oven to 350°F. Grind nuts, sugar and cinnamon in blender or food processor. Combine with egg whites. Drop by teaspoon onto an oiled cookie sheet. Bake 15 minutes. Cookies will be soft; do not overbake.

Makes 15 cookies.

Per cookie: 123 calories, 9.9g total fat (1g saturated), 3g carbohydrate, 2.8g protein, 1g fiber, 9mg sodium.

WHY IT'S GOOD FOR YOU:

* High antioxidants, trace minerals and fiber in walnuts
* Very low saturated fat
* Plus: Walnuts lower cholesterol, protect against heart disease

---

Science Says:

Eating one-and-a-half ounces of walnuts per day as part of a diet low in saturated fat and cholesterol may reduce the risk of heart disease, says the Food and Drug Administration.

Fat-Free Ginger Cookies

1   cup packed brown sugar

1   jar (2.5-ounce) baby-food prunes

¼   cup molasses

¼   cup egg substitute

2¼   cups all-purpose flour

2   teaspoons ground ginger or 2 tablespoons grated fresh ginger for a strong ginger taste

1   teaspoon ground cinnamon

1   teaspoon baking soda

¼   teaspoon ground cloves

¼   cup granulated white sugar

WHY IT'S GOOD FOR YOU:
* Very low fat
* Low calorie
* Antioxidants in prunes and spices
* Plus: Ginger is a mild blood thinner and anti-inflammatory

In a large bowl, beat the brown sugar, prunes, molasses and egg substitute until smooth. Combine the remaining ingredients except the white sugar; thoroughly stir into the wet mixture. Cover and refrigerate at least 2 hours, or overnight.

Preheat oven to 350°F. Spray a cookie sheet with canola or olive oil. Form the dough into small, walnut-sized balls, roll in the sugar and place 2 inches apart on the cookie sheet. Bake 10-12 minutes. Cool on a wire rack.

Makes 4 dozen.

Per cookie: 43 calories, 0.1g total fat, 10g carbohydrate, 0.8g protein, 0.2g fiber, 31mg sodium.

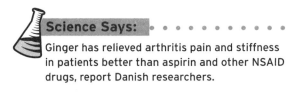

Science Says:
Ginger has relieved arthritis pain and stiffness in patients better than aspirin and other NSAID drugs, report Danish researchers.

Total® Calcium Cookies

4 cups whole-grain Total® cereal

¾ cup quick-cooking oats

2 teaspoons ground cinnamon

1 teaspoon ground ginger

1 teaspoon baking soda

2 beaten eggs or ½ cup egg substitute

1 packed cup brown sugar

1 jar (2.5 ounces) baby-food prunes

1 cup chopped walnuts

WHY IT'S GOOD FOR YOU:

* High vitamins, minerals in Total cereal

* Oats are low glycemic index, suppress blood sugar

* Spices have antioxidant and antibiotic activity

* Plus: Each cookie has 135mg calcium

Preheat oven to 350°F.

Crush Total cereal in a blender until it looks like coarse flour. Add oats, spices, baking soda and stir. In another bowl combine eggs, sugar, prunes, and nuts. Add dry ingredients to wet ingredients and combine thoroughly. Spray a cookie sheet with canola or olive oil. Drop cookies by the teaspoon on the sheet about an inch apart. Bake 10-12 minutes.

Makes about 40 cookies.

Per cookie: 64 calories, 2.3g total fat (0.3.g saturated), 10g carbohydrate, 1.3 g protein, 0.6g fiber, 63mg sodium.

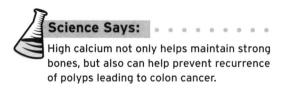

Science Says: . . . .
High calcium not only helps maintain strong bones, but also can help prevent recurrence of polyps leading to colon cancer.

Light Holiday Fruit Cakes

3   egg whites

1   cup unsweetened applesauce

¼   cup fat-free half-and-half

1   teaspoon pure vanilla extract

1   cup no-calorie sweetener such as Splenda

½   cup whole wheat flour

½   cup all-purpose flour

1   teaspoon baking soda

1   tablespoon pumpkin pie spice

1   teaspoon ground cinnamon

½   cup chopped dried pineapple

½   cup dried cranberries, preferably orange flavor

½   cup chopped almonds or walnuts

    Confectioners' sugar for dusting, optional

WHY IT'S GOOD FOR YOU:

* High antioxidants in pineapple, cranberries and applesauce
* Very low calorie, low fat
* Fiber in whole wheat and nuts

Preheat oven to 350°F. In a large bowl, beat egg whites until stiff. Fold in applesauce, half-and-half and vanilla. In a separate bowl, combine Splenda, flour, baking soda and spices. Fold dry ingredients into wet mixture. Fold in pineapple, cranberries and nuts. Spoon batter into nonstick mini-muffin pans greased with cooking spray. Bake 12-15 minutes. Remove, cool. Dust with confectioner's sugar if desired.

Makes 30 cakes.

Per cake: 56 calories, 1.2g total fat (0g saturated), 10g carbohydrate, 1.3g protein, 1g fiber, 54mg sodium.

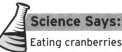

Science Says: • • • • • • • • • • • • • • • •

Eating cranberries helps prevent urinary tract infections by keeping bacteria from sticking to the walls of the bladder. In one test, craisins worked as well as drinking cranberry juice.

• •

Brazil-Nut Stuffed Prunes

20   orange or lemon-scented pitted prunes (dried plums)

20   raw Brazil nuts

¼   cup sugar

1   teaspoon ground cinnamon

Insert a nut into each prune.

Blend sugar and cinnamon.

Roll prunes in sugar. Serve as dessert or snack.

Variation: Stuff prunes with almonds or walnuts.

Makes 20 stuffed prunes.

Per stuffed prune: 56 calories, 3.2g total fat (0.8g saturated), 7g carbohydrate, 0.9g protein, 1.2g fiber, 1mg sodium.

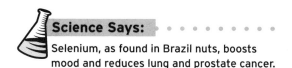

Science Says: Selenium, as found in Brazil nuts, boosts mood and reduces lung and prostate cancer.

Chocolate Fruit-Nut Clusters

1   **cup semisweet chocolate chips**

½   **cup walnut pieces**

¼   **cup raisins**

½   **cup raw oats**

Microwave chocolate chips in a covered bowl on high until melted, 2-3 minutes. Stir until smooth. Add nuts, raisins and oats; combine thoroughly. Drop by teaspoons onto wax paper and cool in refrigerator or freezer until hardened.

Makes 15 clusters.

Per cluster: 96 calories, 5.8g total fat (2g saturated), 12g carbohydrate, 1.5g protein, 0.6g fiber, 1mg sodium.

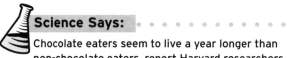

Science Says: • • • • • • • • • •
Chocolate eaters seem to live a year longer than non-chocolate eaters, report Harvard researchers. Dark chocolate especially is high in antioxidants.

• • • • • • • • • • • • • • • • • • • •

Chocolate Prune Surprise

20   pitted prunes (dried plums)

20   whole almonds or walnut halves

1   cup semisweet chocolate chips

Stuff each prune with a nut. Microwave chocolate chips in a covered bowl on high until melted, 2–3 minutes. Stir until smooth. Using two forks, roll each prune in chocolate until lightly covered. Drop onto waxed paper and cool in refrigerator or freezer until hardened.

Makes 20 pieces.

Per piece: 66 calories, 2.9g total fat (1.4g saturated), 11g carbohydrate, 0.7g protein, 0.7g fiber, 1mg sodium.

WHY IT'S GOOD FOR YOU:

* Super high antioxidants in prunes

* High fiber, minerals and good fat in nuts

* Antioxidants in chocolate

 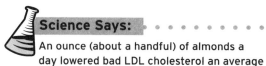

Science Says: • • • • • • • • •
An ounce (about a handful) of almonds a day lowered bad LDL cholesterol an average 4.4 percent in University of Toronto tests.

• • • • • • • • • • • • • • • • •

Ginger Fruit Salad

- 1   8-ounce can crushed pineapple
- 2   kiwis, peeled and sliced
- 1   apple, cored and diced
- 1   cup strawberries, sliced (or whole blueberries)
- ½   cup orange juice
- 1   large banana, sliced
- 1   cup fat-free lemon yogurt
- 2   tablespoons chopped crystallized ginger

WHY IT'S GOOD FOR YOU:

* High antioxidants in pineapple, kiwi, apple, berries and bananas

* Extra high vitamin C in kiwi

* Gut-protecting bacteria in yogurt

Toss fruits and juice together, adding banana just before serving. To serve, put in bowls or parfait glasses, top with yogurt and sprinkle on chopped ginger.

Serves 4.

Per serving: 209 calories, 0.6g total fat, 51g carbohydrate, 3.4g protein, 4.3g fiber, 37mg sodium.

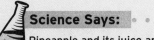

Science Says: • • • • • • • • • • •

Pineapple and its juice are packed with the trace mineral manganese, which can help keep bones strong to prevent osteoporosis.

• • • • • • • • • • • • • • • • • • •

Saucy Summer Fruit Salad

3   **large peaches, peeled and cut into chunks**

1½ **cups blueberries**

1½ **cups sliced strawberries**

2   **bananas, sliced**

1   **tablespoon fresh lemon juice**

Orange-Yogurt Sauce

1   **cup fat-free or low-fat vanilla yogurt**

2   **tablespoons frozen orange juice concentrate**

   Mint sprigs, for garnish

Combine fruit and lemon juice. In a small bowl, mix yogurt and orange juice concentrate. Put fruit into a large glass bowl or 6 small bowls or parfait glasses. Drizzle sauce over fruit and top with mint.

Serves 6.

Per serving: 145 calories, 0.5 g total fat (0.1g saturated), 34g carbohydrate, 3.6g protein, 4.5g fiber, 30mg sodium.

WHY IT'S GOOD FOR YOU:

* High antioxidants in fruits
* Very low fat and low calorie
* Beneficial bacteria in yogurt

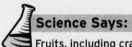

Science Says: • • • • • • • • •
Fruits, including cranberry, apple, red grape, strawberry, peach, lemon, pear, banana, orange, grapefruit and pineapple, retarded the spread of cancer cells in test-tube studies at Cornell.

• • • • • • • • • • • • • • • •

Instant Strawberry Sorbet

1   **pound frozen strawberries (about 3 cups)**

1   **banana, sliced and frozen**

½   **cup fat-free vanilla yogurt**

Put all ingredients in a food processor fitted with the steel blade and process until smooth. Serve immediately.

Serves 4.

Per serving: 90 calories, 0.3g total fat (0g saturated), 22g carbohydrate, 2.3g protein, 0.5g fiber, 23mg sodium.

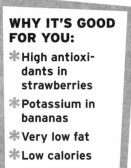

WHY IT'S GOOD FOR YOU:

✳ High antioxidants in strawberries

✳ Potassium in bananas

✳ Very low fat

✳ Low calories

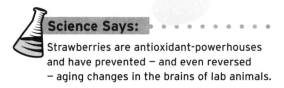

Science Says:

Strawberries are antioxidant-powerhouses and have prevented – and even reversed – aging changes in the brains of lab animals.

Index